The Mathematics of Space Exploration

Myrl H. Ahrendt

Coordinating Editor:
James V. Bernardo, Director
Educational Programs and Services
National Aeronautics and Space Administration

Holt, Rinehart and Winston, Inc., New York

Myrl H. Ahrendt is an Educational Programs Officer at Headquarters of the National Aeronautics and Space Administration, Washington, D.C. Prior to joining the NASA in 1964, he served as Executive Secretary of the National Council of Teachers of Mathematics for twelve years and as a program analyst for the National Science Foundation.

Mr. Ahrendt has taught mathematics in secondary schools in Indiana and was Chairman of Mathematics and Physics Departments, Anderson College, Anderson, Indiana. He has been an instructor in the extension divisions of John Hopkins University, University of Maryland, and the University of Virginia.

He was a delegate to the White House Conference on Education in 1955, served as National President of Sigma Zeta, National Science and Mathematics Society, has held memberships in several professional educational organizations, and is a Fellow of the American Association for the Advancement of Science.

Original drawings: Versatron Corporation

Preface

The ambition to explore space and the attempt to develop the needed science and technology are far from new. Isaac Newton had discovered the basic physical principles and the related mathematics of gravity and satellite behavior as early as 1687. Pioneering work with high-altitude rocket probes was done as early as 1920 by Dr. Robert H. Goddard in the United States and Herman Oberth in Germany. The first V-2 rocket was fired by Germany in 1942. Writers of science fiction have produced many volumes describing imaginary space trips. As part of its contribution to the International Geophysical Year, the United States announced its Vanguard Satellite program in 1955.

The Space Age, and the space race, began in earnest when the Soviet Union orbited Sputnik I on October 4, 1957. The National Aeronautics and Space Administration was born on October 1, 1958. Since then, several hundred satellites have been orbited, an extensive program for the manned exploration of the Moon has been organized, and the exploration of the Solar System and even of deep space are already being planned. Man has crossed the space frontier, and it is inconsistent with his nature to turn back. The result will be profound changes in our viewpoints and manner of living.

The recent developments in the Space Age have special interest for teachers, students, and other persons interested in mathematics. The person who is gifted in mathematics finds motivation in the logic, structure, and beauty of the subject. But many of us have more appreciation of mathematics if we know something of its practical applications. Authors of mathematics textbooks, especially on the secondary level, find it difficult to obtain meaningful and interesting applications. The mathematical study of the mundane problems of taxation, home ownership, and other social situations elicits little en-

3

thusiasm from students who interests in these matters lie quite a few years in the future. Yet these are the applications most commonly offered. Applications of the use of algebra are especially hard to find, since algebra alone is rarely adequate to describe physical and technological phenomena.

The mathematics of space exploration is almost ideally suited to fill this need for meaningful, even exciting, applications. Much of the basic mathematics with which the space scientist or engineer begins can be expressed with linear and quadratic equations like those found in secondary school textbooks. The study and use of these equations helps the reader to better understand space phenomena, and gives him an appreciation of the power of mathematics to help us interpret the physical universe. When a person has expressed a relationship in the language of mathematics, he not only understands the relationship better but he is able to predict the way in which it will behave in every situation in which it will arise. The careful reader of this book will receive new insights into both mathematics and space exploration.

The Space Age presents at least three compelling needs to educators. (1) The steadily growing importance of science and mathematics in our culture make it important that these subjects receive increased emphasis. (2) The scientific manpower needs of our Nation require that we be able to successfully challenge students who have the ability to contribute in these fields. (3) The schools must produce citizens who are literate about the Space Age and its implications. Perhaps this book will make a small contribution to meeting these needs.

Contents

Introduction

Mathematics has always given a sense of excitement and satisfaction to those with an interest in it. "Playing" with mathematics leads continually to the discovery of interesting and unexpected patterns and relationships. No doubt one of the reasons for the appeal of pure mathematics is that its subject matter is unrestricted by the bounds of the physical world. The ideas of mathematics are abstractions. The pure mathematician is not restrained by the requirements of physical utility.

The dawn of the space age also has given to those persons who have an acquaintance with it a deep sense of excitement. The certainty that the exploration of space lies in the years just ahead may well be considered the most exciting and challenging development in the history of man's relationship to his physical environment. Man has already orbited the Earth. Space probes have been sent to the Moon, the planets and the Sun. How soon and how widely man will explore space will depend on how rapidly he is able to acquire the necessary knowledge and technology. We have already crossed the threshold of the space age. Our interests in space exploration are literally "out of this world."

Thus from a philosophical viewpoint it would seem logical that persons who are interested in mathematics would also find it easy to be interested in space. Both are fields of exploration and adventure. Both are challenging to persons who like to pioneer.

From a physical point of view, the relationship of mathematics to the space age is even more intimate since mathematics is the very lifeblood of the space age. Although the pure mathematician is not concerned with the application of his ideas to the physical world, the applied mathematician and the engineer are deeply involved. The systems created by the mathematician have become the language and the instrumentality by which physical relationships are expressed and manipulated. An exact science is impossible without mathematics. In fact, a science becomes exact only when its subject matter becomes sufficiently precise to permit expression of its relationships in mathematical terms. The laws and principles which make space exploration possible are expressed in the language of mathematics. The representation of physical laws in mathematical language not only makes it possible for the engineer to understand and apply them, but it enables him to discover and apply new relationships. The space scientist or engineer would have no means of operating with physical laws and principles if mathematics did not exist.

The Propose and Organization of This Book

This book is not in any sense a book of engineering mathematics. The actual mathematical computations required in the design and operation of space vehicles go far beyond the relatively simple formulas presented in this book. For example, the orbit of a satellite about a perfectly uniform isolated Earth can be described with equations no more difficult than those studied in secondary school mathematics courses. However, in actual practice such ideal orbits do not exist. Every orbit is perturbed by other factors such as the varying density and nonspherical shape of the Earth, the gravity pulls of other bodies, the pressures of radiation and the Solar wind, and the like. Thus, if we wish to follow the exact path taken by a satellite and predict with a high degree of accuracy its location at some future time, computations by an electronic computer are required.

In constructing the outline for this book, two approaches were possible. The book could be structured about topics in mathematics or topics in space science. The latter approach seemed the more satisfactory. Thus the arrangement of the book gives it some continuity as an introduction to space science. The applications of mathematics in the space age overlap many fields of space science. The writer has attempted to give enough background information about the space science topics involved so that the uninformed reader can understand something of the nature and significance of each mathematical application. The author, being a mathematician, is not an authority in any of the many space science topics for which mathematical applications are discussed. However, he has attempted to collect information from authoritative sources, and the background information in the book is believed to be correct. For more complete information about the many interesting facets of space science to which this book alludes, the reader may wish to read some of the other books in this series.

Readers who have completed two or three years of mathematics in high school should be able to use this book with very little difficulty. Readers who find in the book certain topics in mathematics which are new to them will fill in their backgrounds of information by reading the standard textbooks. The basic purpose of this book is to present in simple form enough of the applications of mathematics in the space age to enable the lay person or the student who has a reasonable knowledge of mathematics to form an appreciation and understanding of the role of mathematics in the exploration of space.

How to Use This Book

The book has been liberally sprinkled with problems or exercises called *space flights*. It is hoped that the reader will attempt to take these flights. The solving of these problems will (1) assure that the reader understands the principles discussed; and (2) help him to discover important new relationships. The person who skips the *space flights* will get only part of the information that he should receive. The author has attempted to make these problems not merely exercises in mathematics, but, when possible, discussions of actual space problems. Not all of the *space flights* are easy. Some of them are tricky and will tax your ingenuity. If your background knowledge of mathematics has diminished, a brief review of necessary topics in mathematics will pay dividends in helping you to understand this book and increasing your knowledge of mathematics for use in other areas. We hope that you will enjoy taking these flights. Remember that a good mathematician is not easily discouraged.

A large fraction of the *space flights* in this book call for the finding of squares or square roots. Solving these problems by methods of arithmetic can be very tedious. Tables of squares and square roots will be found in the Appendix. The use of these tables will enable the reader to solve quickly and accurately most of the problems involving roots and powers. A brief table of natural logarithms is included for use in solving the problems in Chapter 4. Occasionally values will be needed which lie between those given in the tables. These in-between values can usually be found with sufficient accuracy by using linear interpolation. (An example of linear interpolation will be found in Chapter 2.) Quick reference to the various formulas and equations can be made by use of the *Summary of Formulas* found in the Appendix. A list of answers to the *space flights* has also been provided. Since numbers obtained by measurement always involve some error, one must be careful in using such approximate numbers not to accept answers which are more accurate than the data from which they were derived. The generally accepted rule is that one should retain in the answer no more significant digits than are found in the least accurate measurements in the data. Most of the measurements used in the *space flights* are correct to three significant digits only. Therefore, most of the answers given have accordingly been rounded to three significant digits.

The author sincerely hopes this book will give you the excitement both of mathematics and of space. The large amount of reading required of the author to become acquainted with these applications was time consuming, but it also was rewarding. It is hoped that the reader will share in these rewards. Mathematics, one of the oldest organized bodies of knowledge, joins hands with and makes possible the newest and most exciting venture of man's hisory. Our wish is that you will become aware of the challenge and adventure of these fields.

1

Motion, Mass, Weight, and Gravity

The Mathematics of Linear Motion

Many of the statements and ideas expressed in this book will be unintelligible to the reader unless he is acquainted with certain laws of motion and with the mathematical equations which express them. Since types of motion are discussed in detail in textbooks of elementary physics, we shall not attempt to give a rigorous or thorough development of these ideas. We shall limit ourselves to an informal discussion of them and illustrate their use with a number of numerical examples.

Velocity, or speed, is a concept which is readily understood by most of us to mean simply distance traveled per unit of time. Although physicists usually make a technical distinction between velocity and speed, we shall use them as synonyms in this book. If we are able to drive 120 miles in three hours in an automobile, we know that the average speed is $\frac{120}{3}$ or 40 miles per hour. The relationship is expressed in general by the equation

$$v_a = \frac{s}{t}, \qquad (1)^*$$

in which the average velocity is v_a, the distance is s, and the time is t. For example, if a jet airplane travels 2300 miles in four hours, the average velocity will be $\frac{2300}{4}$ or 575 miles per hour. We can, of course, apply the principles taught in elementary algebra, and solve the above for s or t as needed.

---

* Equations and formulas listed in the Appendix by number.

When a body starts from rest, it must gain speed for a while to reach a desired velocity. A change in velocity is called an acceleration. Acceleration may be positive or negative. A negative acceleration, or a slowing down, is usually called a deceleration or retardation. If a is the acceleration and v_1 and v_2 are the initial and terminal velocities respectively, the acceleration produced during a time t is expressed by the formula

$$a = \frac{v_2 - v_1}{t}.$$

Thus, if an airplane was flying at a speed of 100 miles per hour and it increased its speed to 300 miles per hour in five minutes, the gain in speed is $300 - 100$, or 200 miles per hour, and the acceleration experienced was 40 miles per hour per minute. If the airplane started from rest, so that $v_1 = 0$, then the formula reduces to the form $a = \frac{v}{t}$, in which v is the terminal velocity. We shall distinguish between average velocity and terminal velocity in the formulas by using the subscript a (for "average") to indicate average velocity. Thus average velocity is indicated by v_a and terminal velocity by v. In most of our problems we shall be concerned with the terminal velocity reached during a period of acceleration. Rearranging the equation $a = \frac{v}{t}$, we obtain

$$v = at. \tag{2}$$

Equation (2) will be used many times in this book. For example, if the airplane gains speed at the rate of 80 miles per hour per minute for five minutes, then the velocity attained at the end of the period of acceleration is $80 \times 5 = 400$ miles per hour.

If we wish to find the distance that a body moving with a constant velocity will travel in a given interval of time, we use the equation obtained by solving equation (1) for s, obtaining

$$s = v_a t. \tag{3}$$

If an automobile travels at an average speed of 45 miles per hour for two hours, the distance traveled will be $s = 45 \times 2 = 90$ miles.

Let us consider again the case in which a body starts from rest and travels with a constant acceleration (that is, with a steadily increasing speed) until it reaches terminal velocity v. Then the average velocity is $\dfrac{0+v}{2}$. That is, $v_a = \frac{1}{2}v$. But $v = at$, by equation (2), and therefore $\frac{1}{2}v = \frac{1}{2}at$. If we substitute this value in formula (3) above,

$$s = v_a t = \tfrac{1}{2}at(t),$$
or
$$s = \tfrac{1}{2}at^2. \tag{4}$$

Since from equation (2) $t = \dfrac{v}{a}$, we obtain by substitution in equation (4) above

$$s = \tfrac{1}{2}a \left(\frac{v}{a} \right)^2$$
or
$$s = \frac{v^2}{2a}, \tag{5}$$

from which we obtain

$$v^2 = 2as. \tag{6}$$

The difference between acceleration and velocity should be clear to all persons who have driven an automobile. When the automobile starts from rest, we depress the "accelerator" pedal to produce a force sufficiently large to move the automobile. It gains speed steadily until it reaches cruising speed. We then "ease up" on the accelerator pedal and give the motor only enough power to keep the car moving at constant speed by overcoming the various sources of friction, such as friction of the tires with the road, of the internal machinery, and of the automobile with the air. If no force were needed to overcome friction, the remainder of the trip would be "free," without the expenditure of additional power. This is precisely what happens to a craft in space when it moves under the influence of gravity. After sufficient force has been applied to place it in an orbit far enough above the atmosphere so that friction with the air no longer is present, the craft will continue indefinitely in a gravitational orbit without the expenditure of further power.

No motion is possible, of course, unless a force acts upon a body to produce it. Every body at rest will remain at rest unless acted upon by some force. The acceleration produced by a force is proportional to the force. This relationship was expressed by Newton in the equation

$$f = ma. \tag{7}$$

Suppose that a mass m is acted upon by a force f to produce an acceleration a. If the same mass m is acted upon by another force F, the acceleration produced will be A. We thus have the equations

$$f = ma$$

and $$F = mA.$$

If we divide the first equation by the second one, we obtain

$$\frac{f}{F} = \frac{a}{A}.$$

If we can determine the acceleration A produced by force F, we can calculate from the above proportion the acceleration produced by another force f. One way in which to determine the acceleration produced by a force is to let a body fall and measure the resulting acceleration. Then the force is the weight of the object, and the acceleration experienced by the falling body is g, the acceleration of gravity. The above equation can then be written as

$$\frac{f}{w} = \frac{a}{g},$$

or $$f = \frac{w}{g}a, \tag{8}$$

in which f is the force in pounds, w is the weight in pounds, g is the acceleration of gravity in feet per second per second, and a is the acceleration produced, measured in feet per second per second. Careful measurements show that the average value of g at the surface of the Earth is approximately 32.2 feet per second per second. (It would seem to be intuitively expected that the gravitational pull of the Earth upon a freely falling body would produce an acceleration. The Earth gives a steady pull, and the falling body begins each new second of fall with the velocity reached during the preceding second. Thus the body falls faster and faster.)

The above equations of motion enable us to understand many physical phenomena related to motion or traveling, and to solve many interesting problems. Suppose a man weighing 150 pounds is riding up in an elevator. The elevator starts from rest and has an upward acceleration of three feet per second during each second. The period of acceleration lasts for three seconds. At the end of this time the elevator will have attained its "cruising" or constant velocity of nine feet per second. The force exerted on the man is, by equation (8),

$$f = \frac{150}{32.2} \times 3 = \frac{450}{32.2} = 14 \text{ pounds.}$$

This means that the man is pushed against the floor of the elevator with a force of 14 pounds. If he were standing on a spring scale, his weight would read 150 + 14 = 164 pounds during the three-second period of acceleration.

If we solve equation (8) for the acceleration a, we obtain

$$a = \frac{f\,g}{w}. \tag{9}$$

This formula enables us to compute the acceleration a that a given force f will produce if it acts on a body with weight w. Let us use this equation to investigate the performance possibilities of one of the commercial jet airliners. The Convair 880 has a maximum take-off weight of 184,500 pounds. Each of its four turbojet engines has a maximum thrust of 11,200 pounds. The force f available to push the airplane forward is $4 \times 11,200$ = 44,800 pounds. The weight to be moved is 184,500 pounds. Substituting these values in equation (9), we find that the maximum acceleration possible is

$$a = \frac{44,800 \times 32.2}{184,500} = \frac{1,442,560}{184,500} = 7.8 \text{ feet per second} \\ \text{per second.}$$

In one minute (60 seconds) the plane will reach a velocity of $60 \times 7.8 = 468$ feet per second or 319 miles per hour. The plane does not perform in a fashion as spectacular as this because a significant part of the thrust or moving force must be used to overcome friction, reducing the acceleration attained.

Space Flights

1-1. An automobile slows down gradually from 50 miles per hour to 20 miles per hour in 10 seconds. What is the rate of deceleration in miles per hour per second? In feet per second per second?

1-2. An automobile traveling 45 miles per hour comes to a complete stop in 10 seconds after the brakes are applied. Find the deceleration in feet per second per second. Find the distance required for stopping. Use equation (4).

1-3. The speedometer of an automobile registers 15 miles per hour at a given instant, and eight seconds later it registers 47 miles per hour. What was the acceleration? What was the distance traveled during this interval?

1-4. An elevator starts from rest and gains speed at the rate of four feet per second per second for two seconds. Then it continues to rise at the rate of eight feet per second. If a man weighing 160 pounds is standing on a spring scale on the elevator, what will the scale read during the first two seconds? After the first two seconds?

1-5. A person weighing 160 pounds stood on a spring scale on an elevator. When the elevator started up, the scale momentarily read 182 pounds, and when the elevator slowed to a stop, the scale for a short instant read 130 pounds. Find the acceleration and deceleration of the elevator.

1-6. If the elevator above were to descend with an acceleration of 32.2 feet per second per second, what would the scale read during the period of acceleration?

1-7. A stone is dropped over a cliff and falls a distance of 1000 feet. It falls, of course, with the acceleration of gravity, 32.2 feet per second per second. Use equation (4) to find out how long it will take the stone to reach the ground. What is its final velocity?

1-8. A Boeing intercontinental jet airplane has a take-off weight of 295,000 pounds and four turbojet engines with a thrust of 18,000 pounds each. Neglecting friction and flight controls, what would be its maximum possible take-off acceleration?

1-9. The Convair jet transport has a rate of climb of about 3,500 feet per minute. At this rate, how long would it take the plane to climb to a cruising altitude of 39,000 feet?

1-10. When a body is dropped, it falls with the acceleration of gravity independent of any horizontal velocity which the body may be given. Thus if an object is dropped from a high building or thrown horizontally from the building, it will reach the ground in the same length of time in either case. The vertical and horizontal actions do not interfere with each other. A bombing plane flying at an altitude of 30,000 feet with a speed of 500 miles per hour drops a bomb. How long will it take the bomb to reach the ground? How far horizontally will the plane travel during this interval?

1-11. Ranger 7, a spaceprobe to the Moon, was orbited by NASA on July 28, 1964. It was designed to crash land on the Moon and to take and transmit to Earth pictures of the Lunar surface during the last 17 minutes of its flight. It was found after launch that it was flying a little too fast and would pass in front of the Moon unless slowed down. Therefore, when Ranger was 101,044 miles out in space, a course correction was applied by radio signal to slow the 806-pound craft through the firing of a 50-pound thrust retrorocket. This reverse thrust slowed Ranger's speed by 67 miles per hour to 3927 miles per hour. What actual firing time in seconds was needed to decrease the velocity 67 miles per hour? Ranger 7 took 4,316 pictures of the Lunar surface, the best ones showing a resolution 2000 times as good as had been possible with Earth-based telescopes. Ranger hit the Moon within 10 miles of the selected aim point.

1-12. The Mercury spacecraft, weighing about 3000 pounds in flight, carried three retrorockets, each producing a thrust of 1000 pounds during a burning time of 10 seconds. They were fired in sequence to slow down the spacecraft in order to initiate a re-entry sequence. What was the total deceleration produced by the firing of the three motors? What was the reduction in velocity?

1-13. The Mercury spacecraft carried three posigrade motors, each having a thrust of 400 pounds and a burning time of one second. They were fired together after burn-out of the final stage to separate the capsule from the booster. What extra velocity did they give to the spacecraft?

The Mathematics of Circular Motion

Practically everyone has at some time whirled an object tied to the end of a string. The whirling object "pulls" on the string, and the greater the speed the stronger the pull. If the string breaks or if we let go of it, the object ceases to follow a circular path and flies off in a straight line tangent to the circle in which it was moving. These facts are illustrated in Figure 1-1. The tendency of any moving object, unless it is affected by external forces, is to continue moving in a straight line. In order to keep a body moving in a circular path, a force directed toward the center of the circle must be supplied to it continuously. The force which kept the above object in a circular path was the tension in the string. This force toward the center is

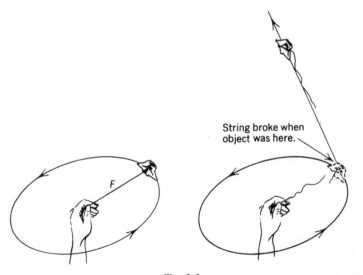

Fig. 1-1

called *centripetal* force. It is shown in textbooks on physics that

$$F = \frac{m \ v^2}{r}, \qquad (10)$$

where F is the centripetal force, m is the mass of the moving object, v is the velocity, and r is the radius of the circle. This form of the equation requires the use of units in the metric system. The outward pull on the string, the reaction to the centripetal force, is called *centrifugal* force. It is convenient when we are using English units of measurement to modify equation (10) by substituting the relationship

$$m = \frac{w}{g}. \qquad (11)$$

The equation then becomes

$$F = \frac{w \ v^2}{gr}, \qquad (12)$$

so that w is the weight of the object in pounds, v is its velocity in feet per second, g is the acceleration of gravity in feet per second per second, r is the radius in feet, and F is the centripetal force in pounds. Let us suppose that an object weighing ½ pound is being whirled at the rate of one revolution per second in a circle of radius two feet. The velocity in feet per second will be the distance traveled in one revolution, or the circumference of the circle, which is $2\pi r$. Then

$$F = \frac{\frac{1}{2}(2 \times 3.14 \times 2)^2}{32.2 \times 2} = 1.22 \text{ pounds}.$$

Thus the tension in the string is 1.22 pounds. If the "breaking strength" of the string is less than this, the string will break and the object will fly out of the circular path.

Space Flights

1-14. If an object weighing 12 ounces is whirled at the end of a three-foot string with a velocity of 10 feet per second, what is the tension in the string?

1-15. A string has a breaking strength of two pounds. It is attached to an object weighing four ounces, which a boy is whirling at a constant angular velocity of two revolutions per second, while gradually letting the string out to increase the radius. At what radius will the string break?

1-16. Show that, assuming a constant angular velocity, the centripetal force is doubled when the radius is doubled.

1-17. A satellite weighing w pounds is orbiting the Earth with a velocity of 4.85 miles per second at a radius of 4060 miles from the center of the Earth. Find the centripetal force which is holding it in orbit. (Further discussion of this problem will be found in Chapter 5.)

Relationship of Mass, Weight, and Gravity

In the two preceding sections of this chapter we have spoken of both *mass* and *weight*. It is vitally important that we understand clearly the relationship between these two concepts. The key to this understanding is found in equation (11),

$$m = \frac{w}{g}.$$

We used this relationship to modify equation (10) to permit computation of centripetal force with English units of pounds and feet. But equation (11) is much more than a convenience for computation. It expresses the fundamental relationship which relates weight and gravity to mass.

By the mass of an object, we mean the amount of material which it contains. The mass of a body is constant and is independent of its location or motion. (We shall find an exception to this statement when we consider Einstein's equations in Chapter 6, since when a body is moving with reference to another body, its mass increases when its velocity increases. But this increase in mass is negligible at the ordinary velocities involved in present space travel.) Weight, on the other hand, is a variable quantity, and the weight of a body is an "accident" of its location.

Our physical perceptions of mass are obtained almost entirely through our experiences with weight. Weight is produced by the pull of gravity. The pull of gravity attracts any body with mass toward the center of the Earth, and the attraction of gravity is constant at a given location. However, we know from experience that not all objects weigh the same at a given location. Lifting a stone requires a certain effort because of its weight; lifting a different nearby stone requires more effort because the second stone has more weight. Since the attraction of gravity is the same in both cases, the difference in weight is the result of a difference in mass. Thus, if one object weighs twice as much as another object at the same location, the first object must have twice as much mass as the second one.

However, an object with a constant mass may have different weights if it is placed in different locations. The strength of the gravitational attraction or pull of the Earth upon another body depends upon the distribution of mass within the Earth and the distance from the center of the Earth. Since the Earth is not of uniform density, gravitational attraction varies somewhat at different locations with the same altitude. The gravitational pull of the Earth is also less at greater distances from the center, so that the Earth pull at the top of mountains is, in general, less than at lower altitudes.

If a mass is moved from the surface of the Earth to the surface of the Moon, its weight will be greatly reduced. Because of the smaller mass of the Moon, the attraction of gravity is about one-sixth that on the Earth. If a location in space with no gravity could be found, or if, as is sometimes suggested in science fiction, the force of gravity could be neutralized, an object, no matter how great its mass, would have no weight at all.

Let us introduce Newton's Law of Universal Gravitation,

$$F = G \frac{M \ m}{d^2}. \tag{13}$$

It will have fundamental applications later in this book, and will also help us here. Note that the d^2 in the denominator tells us that the force of attraction between two bodies varies inversely as the square of the distance between their centers.

We can use this to find the weight of a body in space. Suppose that an object which weighs 100 pounds on the surface of the Earth is moved 3960 miles, the length of the Earth's radius, out into space, so that its distance from the center of the Earth is doubled. At this location in space the surface weight would be divided by 2^2 or 4, and the object would weigh $\frac{100}{4}$ or 25 pounds. In general, if w_s is the weight at the surface of the Earth, r is the radius of the Earth, and w_h is the weight at distance h above the surface, then

$$\frac{w_h}{w_s} = \frac{r^2}{(r+h)^2}$$

or
$$w_h = \left(\frac{r}{r+h}\right)^2 w_s. \tag{14}$$

Let us suppose that the above body, with weight $w_s =$ 100 pounds, had been placed only 1000 miles above the surface of the Earth. Its weight at that altitude would be

$$w_h = \left(\frac{3960}{3960 + 1000}\right)^2 \times 100 = .64 \times 100 = 64 \text{ pounds.}$$

Since the reduced weight of the body in space results from the fact that the gravitational pull of the Earth is less at that point, we could in a similar manner have investigated the value of g at a distance h above the surface of the Earth. We would have obtained an equation identical in form to (14),

$$g_h = \left(\frac{r}{r+h}\right)^2 g_s. \tag{15}$$

In fact, it would have been appropriate for us to consider equation (15) as the more fundamental of the two and from it to have obtained equation (14), since weight is produced by the pull of gravity.

In later chapters we shall compute the acceleration which a given force produces when it acts on a body somewhere in space. Our formula for computing acceleration will be equation (9), $a = \frac{f\,g}{w}$. The question then arises: What value of w

should we use? The answer: It makes absolutely no difference as long as we also use the value of g which applies in that location in space. Remember that the only constant quantity involved is the mass m, and it is always true that $m = \dfrac{w}{g}$. Since the values of w and g at the surface of the Earth will always be known, it is much more efficient, involving less computation, for us to use them rather than to compute additional values of w and g for the particular altitudes involved.

An interesting situation arises when we consider the ratio $\dfrac{w}{g}$ for a body in orbit. Since the centrifugal force resulting from the movement of a body in orbit balances its weight, the body acts as if it had no weight and gravity did not exist. In fact, the popular literature speaks of a body in orbit as being "weightless" and in a "zero g" condition. Thus the ratio $\dfrac{w}{g}$ could be said to equal $\dfrac{0}{0}$. Although we are taught in elementary mathematics that division by zero is excluded, we learn in advanced mathematics that $\dfrac{0}{0}$ can represent a real number. This ratio is one of a group of *indeterminate* forms, and methods for evaluating them are found in the calculus. For a body in orbit we may say that $\dfrac{w}{g} = \dfrac{0}{0} = m$. Thus computations related to bodies in orbit will always be simplified and freed from ambiguity if we use the surface values of w and g.

For the person who wishes to dig more deeply into the application of Newton's law, an interesting point arises. There may be a small error involved when the law is applied to a rotating body such as the Earth. The Earth is rotating at a high velocity, and the materials on its surface at the Equator have a velocity of about 1000 miles per hour. They have a centrifugal tendency which acts against the natural gravitational pull resulting from the mass of the Earth. The "real" Earth pull is the "natural" Earth pull reduced by the centrifugal force produced by the rotation of the Earth. Objects on a rotating Earth, especially near the equator, weigh slightly less than they would weigh on a non-rotating Earth. In a similar manner, the pull on objects above the surface, in space, is slightly less than Newton's law predicts. The law will apply without error only to bodies above the North and South Poles, where no centrifugal force is involved. However, the above error is so small that it is negligible for all ordinary measurements. The values of w_h and g_h predicted by equations (14) and (15) will also be very slightly in error, depending upon the position at which the body is located in space. These formulas assume, of course, that the body is stationary, and do not take into consideration the effects of any motion of the body in space. In every situation the ratio $\dfrac{w}{g} = m$, a constant.

Space Flights

1-18. The ratio of the gravitational attraction at the North Pole to that at Denver, Colorado is $\dfrac{9.832}{9.796}$. If an object weighed 20 pounds in Denver, what would it weigh at the North Pole?

1-19. If an object weighs w pounds on the Earth, what will it weigh 22,300 miles out in space?

1-20. A spacecraft weighing two tons at the surface of the Earth is located 200 miles above the surface. What is its weight at that altitude?

1-21. What change is made in the weight of an object when it is moved from the surface of the Earth to a distance equal to two Earth radii above the surface?

1-22. What is the acceleration of gravity at a point three Earth radii above the surface of the Earth?

1-23. A body weighing one pound is located on the Equator. It is therefore moving at a velocity of about 1,000 miles per hour. Use equation (12) to compute the centrifugal force which the rotation of the Earth gives it. What fraction is this of its weight? Compute from this result the percentage of error in Newton's Law at the Equator.

1-24. A spacecraft with weight w at the Earth's surface is located 215,000 miles, or 54 Earth radii, from the center of the Earth. Express its weight in space as a fraction of its weight on the surface of the Earth. The spacecraft is also 24,000 miles, or 22 Moon radii, from the center of the Moon. Its weight on the surface of the Moon would be $\frac{w}{6}$, since the attraction of gravity on the Moon is one-sixth of that on the Earth. Express the weight of the spacecraft as a fraction of its weight on the surface of the Moon. The two weights should be equal, since the spacecraft is located at the neutral gravitational point between the Earth and the Moon.

1-25. An explanation of how a body remains in orbit is to say that the centrifugal force resulting from its circular motion is equal to its weight at that altitude. In *space flight* 1-17 you computed the centrifugal force for a body with surface weight w in orbit 100 miles above the Earth. Use equation (14) to find the space weight of the body at that altitude. Do your two answers agree? (Remember that centrifugal force is the reaction to and is equal to centripetal force.)

2

Measurements for the Space Age

Nature of Measurement

The level of the technology which a culture can reach is determined in many respects by its ability to make and use precise measurements. However, in an age in which accurate measurement is of fundamental importance, there are many persons who do not understand the nature of measurement. Have you ever wondered about the television or radio announcer who introduces a break for a "commercial" with a statement such as "I'll be back in *exactly* one minute," or about the home buyer who wants his back-yard patio made *exactly* eight feet deep? A time interval of exactly one minute or a length of exactly eight feet has never been established by measurement since time began.

Measurement is always approximate; no measurement is ever exact. Measurement always involves error. We get exact numbers when we count objects. A housewife can buy exactly one dozen eggs, but no one can saw a board so that it is exactly 12 feet long. The approximate nature of measurement is understood by persons or companies who manufacture parts to high degrees of precision. The allowed error, called *tolerance,* is stated on every blueprint. The space age has placed almost incredible precision requirements upon manufacturers of parts and equipment. A few years ago a tolerance of .001 inch was considered exacting. Now manufacturers are asked to deliver parts with tolerances of from one millionth to five millionths of an inch.

In contrast to the high precision requirements placed upon the manufacturers of space parts and equipment, the precision of the measurements used in this book is not high. The engineer designing a spacecraft must obtain results which are

Fig. 2-1. Flawless planning and accurate measurement are vital. (NASA)

much more precise than those which we obtain in working with illustrations of space problems. Although the scientist often prefers to use units of measure from the metric system, the reader will note that the measurements in this book are given in the usual English units of feet, miles, pounds, and the like. We use the units most familiar to the non-scientist because they are used in newspaper stories and other popular literature about space activities.

New Units of Measurement

The reader will find that a discussion of space exploration requires the use of many units of measurement which are likely to be new. Some of them are defined and illustrated below.

Apogee. The point in the orbit of any celestial body or satellite at its maximum distance from the Earth. The apogee distances quoted in the popular literature are measured from the surface of the Earth. However for the sake of greater simplicity and directness the mathematical expressions used will be based upon apogee distances measured from the center of the Earth.

Perigee. The point in the orbit of any celestial body or satellite nearest the Earth. Though the popular literature gives perigee distances measured from the surface of the Earth, the mathematical expressions will be based upon perigee distances measured from the center of the Earth.

Astronomical Unit. The mean (average) distance between the Earth and the Sun, or 93,000,000 miles. It is abbreviated A.U.

Light Year. The distance traveled by light in one mean solar year, or 5.88×10^{12} miles. (Light travels at the rate of 186,300 miles per second.)

Parsec. The distance at which a star would have a parallax of one second of arc. (If we abbreviate the words "parallax of one second," we obtain the term *parsec.*) One parsec equals 3.26 light years or 206,265 A.U.

A brief discussion of the last three units above may aid understanding. Let us first define the term *parallax.* Parallax is the difference in direction which the same object seems to have when viewed from two different points. As an experiment, hold up one finger at arm's length and look at it with one eye. Then cover that eye and look at it with the other eye. You will note that the position of your finger with reference to the background seems to change when it is observed with one eye and then with the other. When you look at an object with two eyes, each sees it from a slightly different angle. Your mind solves a parallax problem whenever you look at an object, and tells you the object's distance. A person blinded in one eye receives no parallax and finds it difficult to judge distances.

When we speak of the parallax of the Moon, or of the Sun, we ordinarily mean the angle measured from the two points pictured in Figure 2-2, in which E is the center of the Earth, M is the position of the Moon, A is a point on the surface of the Earth such that angle EAM is a right angle, and EA is the radius of the Earth. The parallax of the Moon from these posi-

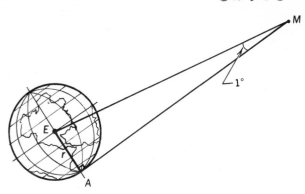

Fig. 2-2

tions is a little less than one degree, and the distance *EM* can readily be calculated by trigonometry.

The stars are so far away, however, that a base line equal to the radius or even the diameter of the Earth is too short. For distant stars, the base line used is the diameter, E_1E_2, of the orbit of the Earth, shown in Figure 2-3. If a star is viewed in July, and six months later in January, when the Earth is half way through its orbit, the star will appear to have shifted its position slightly, enabling the observer to measure the angle of parallax. The distance at which a star will have a parallax of one second of arc ($\frac{1}{3600}$ degree) has been adopted as a unit of measure for great distances. This unit is termed the *parsec*. You will note in Figure 2-3 that the distance E_1S, the radius of the orbit of the Earth, is equal to one Astronomical Unit.

Kiloparsec. A distance of 1000 parsecs, or 3.26×10^3 light years.

Megarparsec. A distance of one million parsecs, or 3.26×10^6 light years.

g. The acceleration produced by the pull of gravity on a freely falling body at the surface of the Earth, causing an increase in speed of 32.2 feet per second during each second of fall. Although *g* is an acceleration and does not exist unless there is motion, the expression "g force" is often used to indicate a force which produces an acceleration measured in

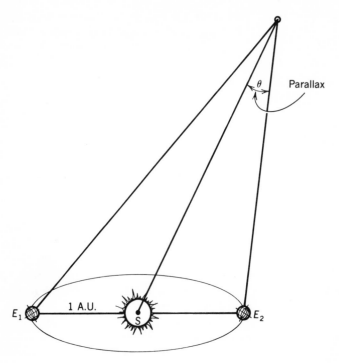

Fig. 2-3

g's. Used in this sense, one g is a force which will produce an acceleration of 32.2 feet per second per second. A force of two g's will produce an acceleration of 2 × 32.2 or 64.4 feet per second per second.

A pull of one g gives a body its "normal" weight. Doubling the pull of gravity doubles the weight. Thus a man who ordinarily weighs 160 pounds would, if subjected to an acceleration of three g's, feel and act as if his weight had been increased to 480 pounds. A rocket boosting a spaceship into orbit has brief periods of acceleration as much as eight to ten g's. With an acceleration of eight g's, the rocket is gaining speed at the rate of 8 × 32.2 or about 258 feet per second during each second. The astronaut in the spacecraft feels, and acts, as if his weight had been multiplied by eight.

A human can stand brief periods of acceleration of up to 20 *g*'s. However, if he attempted to take such high accelerations in a standing or sitting position, his body might be injured and certainly the blood would be drained from his brain, leading to quick unconsciousness. Therefore an astronaut on take-off and re-entry lies down in a couch and takes the *g* forces in the easiest and safest way.

Mach Number. The ratio of the velocity of a moving object to the velocity of sound in that same portion of the atmosphere. Mach 2 denotes a speed twice that of sound.

The Mach number is a relative rather than an absolute measure of speed; it merely compares the speed of an object with the speed of sound in that portion of the atmosphere through which the object is moving. The speed of sound in dry air at ordinary temperatures is approximately 1100 feet per second, or 750 miles per hour. These values should be used in solving the *space flights* in this book. The speed of sound in general increases (or decreases) as the temperature of the air increases (or decreases). Thus speeds equal in Mach numbers would not necessarily be equal in miles per hour, and vice versa. Since a supersonic speed is one which is greater than the speed of sound, a speed greater than Mach one is supersonic.

Nautical Mile. The length of one minute of arc on a great circle of the Earth. A nautical mile equals 6080 feet, or approximately $\frac{38}{33}$ statute mile.

Statute Mile. The ordinary mile, equal in length to 5280 feet. (Whenever the word *mile* is used in this book, it refers to the statute mile.)

Space Flights

2-1. Find the number of astronomical units in one light year.

2-2. Express the parsec in miles.

2-3. Express the length of the astronomical unit in miles.

2-4. The distance to the Moon is about 239,000 miles. What fraction of an A.U. is this?

2-5. How many nautical miles are there in the circumference of the Earth?

2-6. Find the number of light years in 9 parsecs. In 7.3 parsecs.

2-7. How many parsecs are there in 21 light years? In one?

2-8. A typical cruising speed for a commercial jet passenger plane is 600 miles per hour. Express this speed as a Mach number.

2-9. Find the speed of Mach 2.5 in feet per second. In miles per hour. In nautical miles per hour.

2-10. A pilot weighing 170 pounds is subject to an acceleration of 3 g's. What is the weight his body feels?

2-11. If a pilot experiences an acceleration of 200 feet per second per second, what is the weight his body feels?

2-12. Some automobile manufacturers rate their motors in terms of the number of seconds required to begin at a standing start and get the automobile to a speed of 60 miles per hour. If the automobile can reach 60 miles per hour in 10 seconds, it experienced a gain in velocity (an acceleration) of six miles per hour during each second. Find the gain in velocity in feet per second per second. What fraction of a g is this acceleration?

2-13. A vehicle gains speed at the rate of 322 feet per second per second. What is the acceleration in g's?

2-14. During the flight of John H. Glenn, Jr., in *Friendship 7*, a Mercury spacecraft, the "g force" built up from one g at the beginning of launch to 6.7 g's when the booster engine in the first stage cut off at the end of 2 minutes 10 seconds of powered flight. At what rate in feet per second per second was the spacecraft accelerating at cut-off in stage one? During the burning of the second stage, lasting 2 minutes 52 seconds, the "g force" went from 1.4 g's to 7.7 g's. What was the acceleration at cut-off in stage two?

2-15. The force of one g at the beginning of launch was evidently the normal pull of gravity, so the increase in acceleration during the burning of the first stage was 5.7 g's. If we assume the increase in acceleration was constant, the average increase would have been 2.85 g's. What velocity would this average acceleration produce during the interval of two minutes 10 seconds?

2-16. When John Glenn re-entered the atmosphere, atmospheric resistance caused deceleration of the capsule, while the inertia of his body tended to keep him moving at a constant velocity, pushing him into the couch with a force of 7.7 g's. If his normal body weight was 160 pounds, what weight did he feel during the period of greatest deceleration?

2-17. The capsule of John Glenn experienced a brief pull of 3.7 g's when the main parachute deployed during re-entry. What deceleration in feet per second per second was caused by the opening of the parachute?

Measuring the Earth

One of the first space-minded mathematicians in history was a young Greek named Eratosthenes. About 200 B.C., when most people assumed the Earth to be flat, he measured its circumference. Eratosthenes knew that on a certain day of the year the Sun was directly over Assouan, because he saw its reflection in the bottom of a well located there. He further knew that at this time the Sun's rays made an angle of about 7⅕ degrees with a pyramid located at Alexandria, about 500

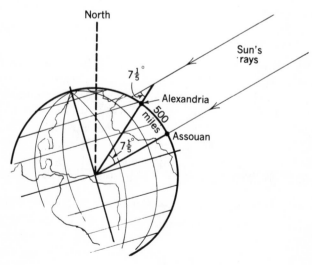

Fig. 2-4

miles north of Assouan, as illustrated in Figure 2-4. Eratosthenes reasoned that the angle at the center of the Earth would also be 7⅕ degrees. Since 7⅕ divides into 360 just 50 times, he reasoned that the circumference of the Earth must be about 50 times 500 miles, or about 25,000 miles.

Measuring the Distance to the Horizon

It is important to be able to compute the distance from a given altitude to the horizon. Let us suppose, in Figure 2-5, that an observer is at point P, an altitude h from the surface of the Earth. Let O be the center of the Earth, with radius $OA = r$. The horizon is located at A, the point where the line of sight from P is tangent to the surface of the Earth. Let us call the distance PA to the horizon d. Since the line PA is tangent to the circle at A, triangle POA is a right triangle. By the Pythagorean equation

$$r^2 + d^2 = (r + h)^2$$
$$d^2 = (r + h)^2 - r^2$$
$$= r^2 + 2rh + h^2 - r^2$$
$$= 2rh + h^2.$$
$$d = \sqrt{2rh + h^2}.$$

It is apparent that in nearly all cases h will be small compared with r, so that h^2 will by comparison be an extremely small quantity. Neglecting it will scarcely change the value of d. If we neglect h^2, we can rewrite the equation as $d = \sqrt{2rh}$. Ordinarily, measurements related to the size of the Earth would be made in miles. However, since h is small, it may be convenient to rearrange the equation so that the altitude can be expressed in feet. Let h_f be the altitude in feet. Then, since h is the altitude in miles, $h_f = 5280\,h$, or $h = \dfrac{h_f}{5280}$. Let $r = 3960$ miles. The equation then becomes

$$d = \sqrt{\frac{2 \times 3960 \times h_f}{5280}}$$

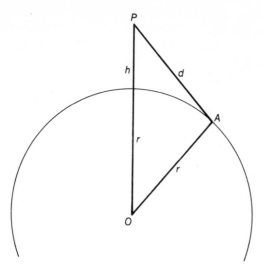

Fig. 2-5

or $$d = \sqrt{1.5\,h_f}.$$ (16)

That is, if the altitude is given in feet, the formula gives the distance to the horizon in miles. If the observer is 100 feet above the surface of the Earth, the distance to the horizon is $\sqrt{150}$ or 12.2 miles.

Space Flights

2-18. Suppose the pyramid in Figure 2-4 had been located 300 miles north of Assouan, instead of 500 miles north at Alexandria. What angle would the Sun's rays have made with the pyramid?

2-19. Find the distance to the horizon for an altitude of 150 feet. 1000 feet. One mile.

2-20. During Gordon Cooper's space flight in *Faith 7* on May 15–16, 1963 a high intensity xenon light was illuminated continuously while the spacecraft was in range on its sixth orbit. If Cooper had been able to see the light as soon as it appeared on the horizon, how far away would it have beén? His average altitude was 133 miles.

2-21. Compute the distance to the horizon from an altitude of 100 miles using the simplified formula (16) and also by using the equation which does not neglect the value of h^2. How much error is introduced at this altitude by using the simplified formula?

2-22. It is convenient in solving many problems in this book to be able quickly to convert feet per second to miles per hour, and vice versa. If you multiply n feet per second by 3600, the number of seconds in an hour, you will obtain the number of feet per hour. If you then divide by 5280, the number of feet in a mile, you will obtain miles per hour. Simplify the resulting ratio to obtain a convenient multiplier for quickly changing feet per second to miles per hour. What would the multiplier be for changing miles per hour to feet per second?

3

The Nature of Space

The Atmosphere

We know that on the Earth we are living at the bottom of a vast ocean of air. This ocean of air, the atmosphere, is both a protector and supporter of life on the Earth. Without its protection we would be alternately frozen and scorched as our portion of Earth turned away from or toward the Sun. The atmosphere protects us from bombardment by meteors and cosmic rays, keeps the oceans from evaporating into space, and provides oxygen and carbon dioxide for support of the life cycle.

We are so accustomed to having air about us that we do not ordinarily think of it as having either volume or weight. But it supports the weight and makes possible the flight of giant aircraft. When it moves with high velocity, as during storms, it demolishes buildings and uproots trees. We are taught in science classes that the atmosphere exerts a pressure of about 14.7 pounds per square inch at sea level. This means a column of air with a cross section of one square inch in area extending from sea level up to the top of the atmosphere weighs 14.7 pounds. We learn in science or physics classes that a column of water 33 feet high or a column of mercury 30 inches high would have the same weight. We have adopted as a convenient means of measuring air pressure the measurement of the height of the column of mercury which balances the weight of the column of air at a given point.

Since the pressure of the air at sea level is produced by the weight of the great sea of air above us, it is apparent that air pressure decreases with altitude. There is no simple mathematical expression within the scope of this book which relates air pressure to altitude. We know that about half of

the air by weight is within 3¼ miles of the surface of the
Earth. Furthermore, the pressure is halved for about each 3¼
miles of additional ascent.

We can easily write a general expression which relates air
pressure to altitude according to this rule. Let P be the pressure in pounds per square inch, while A is the accompanying
altitude in miles. Then

$$P = (14.7)(\tfrac{1}{2})^{\frac{A}{3\frac{1}{4}}}. \tag{17}$$

To test this equation, let us apply it to several cases. When

$A = 3\frac{1}{4}$, $P = (14.7)(\tfrac{1}{2})^{\frac{3\frac{1}{4}}{3\frac{1}{4}}} = (14.7)(\tfrac{1}{2})^1 = 7.35$, as we ex-

pected. When $A = 6\frac{1}{2}$, $P = (14.7)(\tfrac{1}{2})^{\frac{6\frac{1}{2}}{3\frac{1}{4}}} = (14.7)(\tfrac{1}{2})^2 =$
$(14.7)(\tfrac{1}{4}) = 3.68$, again as was expected.

Although this formula is not accurate enough for engineering purposes, it gives results which agree fairly well with actual measurements near the surface of the Earth. It yields
pressures a little too small at altitudes below 10 miles, a little
too large at altitudes between 10 miles and 30 miles, and a
little too small again at altitudes above 30 miles. However,
since the formula is both mathematically interesting and accurate enough for our purposes, we shall use it for solving a
number of problems.

Obviously, the formula is rather easy to use when A is an
integral (whole) multiple of 3¼, since then only integral
powers of 2, which we can readily obtain by direct multiplica-
tion, are needed for the solution of problems. When A is not
an integral multiple of 3¼, we need to find values corresponding to fractional powers of two. Our solutions can be obtained
through the use of logarithms, or by interpolation between
values obtained for integral powers. An illustration follows:

Find the air pressure at an altitude of 20,000 feet. Since
3¼ miles equals 17,160 feet, the ratio $\dfrac{A}{3\frac{1}{4}} = \dfrac{20,000}{17,160} = 1.16$. We
therefore wish to find the value of $(14.7)(\tfrac{1}{2})^{1.16}$. We know
that the value of P corresponding to the exponent 1.16 lies

between the values for exponents one and two. We arrange our computation as follows.

$$.16\left[{}_1\left[\begin{matrix}1\\1.16\\2\end{matrix}\right.\right.\quad\left.\begin{matrix}7.35\\x\\3.68\end{matrix}\right]3.67\left.\right].16\times3.67=.59$$

$$x = 7.35 - .59 = 6.76$$

Since the exponent 1.16 lies .16 of the way between exponents 1 and 2, we assume that the corresponding value lies .16 of the way between 7.35 and 3.68. In other words, .59 represents .16 of the difference between 7.35 and 3.68. We then obtain a pressure of 6.76 pounds per square foot for an altitude of 20,000 feet.

Except for variations in the amount of water vapor, the composition of the atmosphere is practically constant up to a height of at least 60 miles, consisting of 78 percent nitrogen, 21 percent oxygen, and 1 percent of other gases. The lower portion of the atmosphere, called the troposphere, extends to altitudes of 5½ to 11 miles, depending on the latitude. The troposphere is the portion of the atmosphere in which "weather" occurs. It is the layer where rain, snow, clouds, and storms are found. Temperatures vary greatly in the troposphere, with the average temperature at the top being about −56 degrees Centigrade. Rising and descending currents in the troposphere cause much turbulence for the aviator.

The stratosphere begins where the troposphere ends and extends to a height of about 30 miles. This layer of air is free of "weather," has a fairly constant temperature, and is characterized by steady winds with little turbulence. Flying is usually smooth in the stratosphere. The next layer, the mesosphere, extends to an altitude of 50 miles, and, like the troposphere, is characterized by turbulent air. Above the mesosphere and extending for several hundred miles into space is the ionosphere, named after the electrically charged particles it contains. It reflects radio waves back to the Earth, making possible long-distance radio communication. Above the ionosphere, and blending into outer space, is the exosphere.

Space Flights

3-1. What is the air pressure (weight of the air) in tons upon one square foot of the Earth's surface at sea level? (Since one square foot contains 144 square inches, you should multiply 14.7 by 144.)

3-2. What is the air pressure upon one square foot at an altitude of 3¼ miles?

3-3. What is the air pressure in pounds per square inch at the top of Mount Everest with an elevation 5½ miles above sea level?

3-4. Find the total weight in tons of the Earth's atmosphere. (We have computed the weight per square foot and we can compute the surface area of a sphere with the formula $A = 4\pi r^2$. The radius of the Earth is 3960 miles.)

3-5. Oxygen weighs about 1.14 times as much as nitrogen. Thus if the 78 parts of nitrogen weigh one unit each, the total weight of the nitrogen would be 78 units, while the 21 parts of oxygen weighing 1.14 units each would weigh a total of 24 units. Assuming that the remaining gases weigh one unit, the oxygen in the air at sea level constitutes by weight 24 parts out of 103. What is the pressure in pounds per square inch of the oxygen in the air at sea level? Of the nitrogen?

3-6. Find the approximate altitude which would be above 99 percent of the atmosphere.

3-7. If a barometer reads 28 inches of mercury, what is the air pressure at that location in terms of pounds per square inch?

3-8. Many readers have undoubtedly made the trip, by automobile or cog railroad, to the top of Pike's Peak in Colorado. The elevation at the top is 14,108 feet above sea level. What is the air pressure in pounds per square inch at the top of the peak?

Readers who have visited in high mountains, or who have traveled through passes over the Continental Divide in the Rocky Mountains, have quite likely noted that the thinness of the atmosphere and the resulting shortage of oxygen make even mild exercise fatiguing. Persons who move to higher altitudes may require a long period of time to adjust to the new atmospheric environment, and some individuals never seem able to make the adaptation. The body seems to be able to adjust itself to reduced atmospheric pressure more readily than it does to a reduced supply of oxygen. One can tolerate low pressures more readily with supplies of oxygen.

In the rarefied portions of the upper atmosphere and in the hard vacuum of space beyond the atmosphere, no astronaut could survive without a space suit. Above 40,000 feet it is necessary to breathe pure oxygen to maintain consciousness. Above 62,000 feet the blood and other body fluids "boil" because of the reduced pressure, and at still higher altitudes the body might virtually explode. The space suit worn by an astronaut is vital to his existence. It must perform numerous important functions including: maintaining correct pressure; supplying oxygen and removing carbon dioxide and water vapor; allowing free movement of the limbs; maintaining tolerable temperature and humidity conditions; providing a method of communication; and providing a clear view while protecting against radiation and direct sunlight. A satisfactory pressure for a space suit is that which enables the astronaut by breathing pure oxygen to experience the same rate of intake of oxygen that he would experience in the normal atmosphere at the Earth's surface. The U.S. Mercury spacecraft, however, were pressurized with pure oxygen at five pounds per square inch. Recent Russian manned spacecraft have used sea-level pressure with an atmosphere of oxygen and nitrogen similar to that found at sea level.

Space Flights

3-9. What pressure in a spacesuit would enable an astronaut breathing 100 percent oxygen to have the same intake of oxygen which he would have at sea level, where the pressure is 14.7 pounds per square inch and 21 percent of the air is oxygen?

3-10. Find the altitude which would correspond to the above pressure.

3-11. What percent of the air is oxygen at an altitude of 15,000 feet?

3-12. What is the pressure of the oxygen in the air at an altitude of 6½ miles?

3-13. What is the approximate air pressure per square inch at the top of the stratosphere?

3-14. The total skin surface of an average adult is about 18 square feet. If the dimensions of a space suit are made, for freedom of movement, an average of 1⅙ times those of the astronaut, what would be the total surface area of the suit? What would be the total force in pounds against the inside surface of the suit if it is pressurized for 6½ miles? (It is shown in courses in physics that pressure in any fluid, such as air, is exerted equally in all directions. Remember that the surface area varies as the square of the linear dimension.)

3-15. At what atmospheric pressure, 62,000 feet altitude, will the body fluids begin to boil?

3-16. When a Mercury astronaut breathed pure oxygen at five pounds per square inch, by what percent was his consumption of oxygen increased or decreased in comparison with his normal breathing at sea level?

Space Hazards

Travelers in space will be subjected to at least two hazards, about which we have scant information. The first hazard is due to cosmic rays. Cosmic rays are particles of high energy which enter the solar system from the depths of space. They are believed to consist mostly of nuclei of the heavier atoms. On Earth we are largely shielded from these rays by the atmosphere.

There are two radiation belts of high intensity just outside the Earth's atmosphere. These belts, named after James Van Allen who studied them, are composed of ionized particles from the Sun. Since they are electrically charged, they are trapped and held by the magnetic field of the Earth. Figure 3-1 pictures a cross section of the belts. It is noted that they are symmetrical to the Geomagnetic Axis of the Earth. The

magnetic poles, which mark the intersection of the Geomagnetic Axis with the surface of the Earth, are near to but
do not coincide with the North and South Poles. The drawing
shows the intensities of the belts in actual number of counts
per second made by a Geiger counter. It will be noted that
the belts, extending out about 10 Earth radii into space, are
least intense along the Earth's Geomagnetic Axis.

The second space hazard is fast-moving particles of rock,
metal, or dust called meteors or meteorites. It has been estimated that up to 10^8 visible meteors enter the Earth's atmosphere every 24 hours. Most of these are extremely small particles like sand or dust. The frictional heat produced when they
reach the Earth's atmosphere is sufficient to vaporize them.
So-called shooting stars are meteorites which glow because
they are burning up in the Earth's atmosphere. It is estimated
that only about 12 such particles per day survive until they
reach the surface of the Earth. Occasionally large meteors

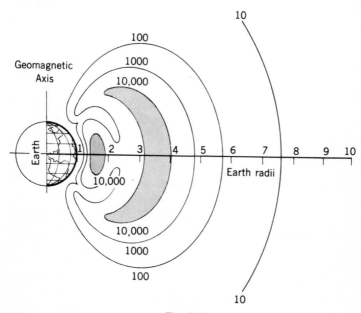

Fig. 3-1

have survived their trip through the atmosphere and have left upon impact huge craters in the surface of the Earth. It is estimated that meteors enter the Earth's atmosphere with velocities ranging from eight to 45 miles per second.

If a spacecraft were to collide with a meteor in space, the danger to the ship would be obvious. A collision with a meteor larger than a grain of sand is so remote that it need not be considered; the chances of its occurrence are about once in every 10,000 years. However, a collision with a tiny particle might, because of the very high speed of the particle, cause the hull of the spaceship at the point of contact to be raised to a temperature of over 1 million degrees. As a result, a hole could be burned in the hull, with disastrous consequences for the occupants. It is possible that protection against collisions with small particles can be obtained by providing an outer skin of metal around the ship.

Other space hazards about which we know little are the biological and psychological hazards associated with weightlessness, prolonged physical inactivity, and the effects of confinement for long periods of time in a closed system.

Space Flights

3-17. If a meteorite and a spacecraft collided head on, the maximum velocity of the collision would be the sum of the individual velocities. The maximum velocity of a spacecraft leaving Earth would be approximately the escape velocity of 7 miles per second, computed in Chapter 5. Using this figure and the data given above, compute the maximum impact velocity of a head-on collision with a meteorite.

3-18. What would be the minimum velocity with which a spacecraft escaping from Earth and a meteorite could collide?

3-19. About how many particles from space survive the trip through the atmosphere and reach the surface of the Earth during a year?

3-20. If a space flight to the Moon is to be made, what direction of take-off would give the astronauts the least exposure to the radiation belts?

3-21. At which of the following altitudes for circular orbits about the Earth would there be the least exposure to radiation? 100 miles. Seven Earth radii. 8500 miles. 18,000 miles. 50,000 miles. Which of these altitudes would provide the greatest exposure?

The Solar System

The Solar System has assumed new meaning for us with the exploration of space progressing. The most familiar object in the Solar System is, of course, the Earth, the space station upon which we live. We have been quite aware of the Sun, the source of the heat and light which make life on Earth possible. The romantically inclined have been attracted by the Moon, and many persons with more than average interest in the heavens have taken pleasure in observing Venus in the evening sky. Now that man's scientific and technological knowledge has progressed to the point where he can expect to conquer the barriers of space, his interest in the Solar System will necessarily increase since the first space trips will be made to the bodies nearest us. If all we know of the Solar System were printed in a single volume, we should have a very large book. One purpose of this discussion is to give some numerical data about the Solar System and to indicate some of the interesting mathematical problems which can be and must be solved as we go about exploring it.

The Solar System consists of one star, the Sun, nine planets, 31 known moons, and many thousands of smaller bodies called asteroids. The nine planets are satellites of the Sun, and they revolve about the Sun in exactly the same way in which we have been able to make artificial satellites revolve about the Earth. The moons are satellites of the planets. The body in the Solar System in which we are most interested at the present time is our own Moon.

All of the planets move in the same direction around the Sun. As we shall find in Chapter 5, their orbital speeds are greatest near the Sun and decrease as the distance from the Sun increases. The paths of the planets are near circles. That is, they are ellipses with small eccentricity. (Eccentricity will

Fig. 3-2. The moon, a major national goal in space exploration.
(NASA)

be discussed in Chapter 5.) All of the planets lie very nearly
in the same plane. Pluto is the notable exception to this rule
with the plane of its orbit tilted about 17 degrees to the plane
of the Earth's orbit. The Solar System is, therefore, shaped
something like a pancake. The general appearance of the
Solar System is indicated in Figure 3-3.

The table on page 47 gives comprehensive and detailed numerical data about the Solar System. With this information the
reader can make many interesting comparisons and solve
many important problems about the Solar System and its relationship to the exploration of space. One piece of information
should be added which does not fit into the format of the

DATA ON THE SOLAR SYSTEM

Body	Diameter (miles)	Mass (Earth = 1)	Density (water = 1)	Period of Revolution	Surface Gravity (Earth = 1)	Average Distance from Sun (millions of miles)	Eccentricity of Orbit	Surface Escape Velocity (miles per second)
Earth	7,920	1	5.52	365 days	1	93	.017	6.9
Jupiter	88,640	317	1.34	11.9 years	2.64	483	.048	37
Mars	4,200	.11	3.96	1.88 years	.39	141.5	.093	3.2
Mercury	3,100	.04	3.8	88 days	.26	36	.206	2.2
Moon	2,160	.012	3.33	27⅓ days	.17	—	.054	1.5
Neptune	31,000	17.2	1.58	165 days	1.12	2,793	.009	14
Pluto	?	.8	?	248 years	?	3,670	.248	?
Saturn	74,500	95	.71	29.5 years	1.07	886	.056	22
Sun	864,000	330,000	1.41	—	28	0	—	387
Uranus	32,000	14.7	1.27	84 years	.91	1,782	.047	13
Venus	7,700	.81	4.86	225 days	.86	67	.007	6.4

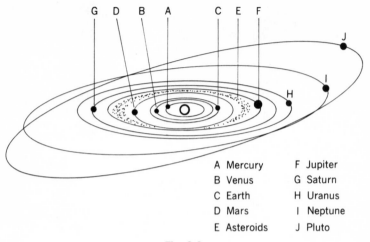

Fig. 3-3

table. This is the average distance from the Earth to the Moon. The distance is approximately 239,000 miles when measured between their centers. It is interesting to note that if the Earth could be placed at the center of the Sun, the Moon would be only half way out to its circumference. In other words, the diameter of the Sun is nearly double the diameter of the orbit of the Moon.

The table giving data on the Solar System will be largely self-explanatory if careful attention is paid to the explanations at the head of each column. The meaning of the numbers in the last two columns, eccentricity and escape velocity, will be explained in further detail in subsequent chapters.

Space Flights

3-22. What percent of the total mass of the Solar System is concentrated in the Sun?

3-23. What bodies, excluding the Moon and the Sun, are the largest and smallest respectively in the Solar System?

3-24. Which planet most closely resembles Earth in diameter, mass, density, period of revolution, surface gravity, and escape velocity?

3-25.. Which planet most closely resembles the Moon in diameter, mass, density, surface gravity, and escape velocity?

3-26. Rank the planets by distance from the Sun and by length of period of revolution. Does there seem to be a similarity? Are there exceptions?

3-27. How long does it take light from the Sun to reach the Earth? (The speed of light is given in Chapter 2.)

3-28. A radar wave travels with a speed equal to the speed of light. How long would it take for a radar signal to be sent from Earth to the Moon and reflected back to Earth?

3-29. Derive a formula like the one in Chapter 2 for finding the distance to the horizon from an altitude above the Moon?

3-30. Use the above formula to find the distance to the horizon from an altitude of 100 feet above the surface of the Moon. From an altitude of 60 miles.

Orbital Velocity

The velocity of a planet in its orbit can be calculated if we know the radius of the orbit and the length of time required to traverse it. The radius of the Earth's orbit is 93×10^6 miles, and the time required to make one complete orbit is 365 days. The length of the orbit is $2\pi r$, which in terms of miles is $2(3.14)(93 \times 10^6)$. The number of seconds required for an orbit is the number of days times the number of hours in a day times the number of seconds in an hour, or $(365)(24)(3600)$. The velocity then equals, by equation (1), $\dfrac{2(3.14)(93 \times 10^6)}{(365)(24)(3600)}$ = 18.3 miles per second. That is, the velocity of the earth in its orbit around the Sun is 18.3 miles per second.

The Third Law of Kepler

John Kepler discovered a remarkable law which states that the squares of the periods of any two planets are to each other as the cubes of their respective distances from the Sun. This law can be stated mathematically as

$$\frac{P^2}{p^2} = \frac{D^3}{d^3}, \tag{18}$$

where P and D represent respectively the period and distance from the Sun for one planet, while p and d represent these quantities for the second planet. Let us use the Earth for the second planet. If the period of the Earth is given in years and its distance from the Sun is given in Astronomical Units, then

$p = 1$ and $d = 1$, reducing the formula to $\dfrac{P^2}{1} = \dfrac{D^3}{1}$,

or $P^2 = D^3$

We can read readily from the table on page 47 that for Mars, $P = 1.88$, while $D = \dfrac{141.5}{93} = 1.52$. We find by computation, or from a table of powers, that $P^2 = 3.5$ and $D^3 = 3.5$. Similarly for Uranus, $P = 84$ while $D = \dfrac{1782}{93} = 19.2$. We find that $P^2 = 7056$, while $D^3 = 7078$. The fact that the numbers do not agree precisely is a result of the fact that for ease of computation we have severely rounded our data. Kepler's law holds for Mars and Uranus.

Space Flights

3-31. Find the orbital velocity in miles per second of Mercury, Mars, Uranus, and Neptune. Do your results verify the statement that the orbital velocity becomes less as the radius of the orbit increases?

3-32. Verify that Kepler's law holds for Jupiter and Saturn.

Newton's Law of Universal Gravitation

The table on page 47 shows that the surface gravities vary a great deal among the bodies in the Solar System. Gravity is the force which holds us on the Earth, the direction of gravitational force always being, of course, toward the center of the Earth. Gravity holds the Earth together, and holds us, our physical structures, oceans, and atmosphere to its surface. The gravitational attraction of the Sun holds the planets in their orbits. No one knows what produces the attraction of gravity, but everyone has experienced its effects. Information about the way in which gravity keeps satellites and the planets in their orbits is given in Chapter 5.

Newton's Law of Universal Gravitation, $F = G\dfrac{M\,m}{d^2}$, equation (13), was mentioned in Chapter 1. If M and m are the masses of two bodies, d is the distance between their centers of gravity, and G is the constant of universal gravitation, then F is the force which attracts the bodies to each other. According to Newton's law, every body in the Universe attracts every other body. The value of G, the gravitational constant, has been measured many times by physicists. It is assumed to be constant for all bodies in the Universe. It should not be confused with g, the acceleration of gravity. As is apparent from equation (13), gravitational attraction is greater when the bodies are of large mass. Also, as we noted in Chapter 1, gravitational attraction varies inversely as the square of the distance between the two masses.

We shall find many additional applications of Newton's Law of Gravitation. We use it to study the surface gravities of the planets. Suppose we compare the surface gravity of the Moon with that of the Earth. We place a unit mass on the surface of the Earth. The distance between the centers of the two masses, the unit mass and the Earth, is 3960 miles. Let F_e be the force of attraction. Let M be the mass of the Earth and m be the mass of the unit mass. Since m is a unit mass, $m = 1$. Then by Newton's law,

$$F_e = \frac{GM(1)}{(3960)^2}.$$

The mass of the Moon is .012 times the mass of the Earth, or .012 M. The radius of the Moon is 1080 miles. Let F_m be the force which attracts the unit mass and the Moon to each other. By Newton's law,

$$F_m = \frac{G(.012M)(1)}{(1080)^2}.$$

The ratio of the Moon's gravity to that of the Earth is then found by dividing this last equation by the one preceding it. Dividing and simplifying yields

$$\frac{F_m}{F_e} = \frac{.012M}{(1080)^2} \times \frac{(3960)^2}{M} = \frac{188,179}{1,166,400} = \frac{1}{6}.$$

This result means that an object which weighs six pounds on the Earth would, if weighed by an Earth scale, weigh only one pound on the Moon. (It is important that our Earth scale be a spring scale, since a balance scale which only compares masses would not reveal differences in weight caused by differences in gravity. Both the mass being weighed and the control mass would be equally affected by a change in gravity.) A man weighing 160 pounds on the Earth would weigh $\frac{1}{6}$ as much or about 27 pounds on the Moon. If a man were able to lift a load weighing 200 pounds on the Earth, he would be able to lift six times as much or the equivalent of 1200 pounds on the Moon.

Thus seemingly incredible feats of strength could be performed on the Moon, far outshining the feats of so-called "strong" men on Earth. Athletes would be able to set fabulous new records for jumping, weight lifting, and the like on the Moon. One must be careful, however, not to overlook elusive facts. For example, suppose that an athlete engaged in a high-jumping contest on Earth is able to clear a bar six feet above the surface. Would he be able to high jump 36 feet on the Moon? If we study the performance of a high jumper, we can see that such an achievement would be impossible. When the athlete starts his jump on the surface of the Earth, his center of gravity is already about four feet above the ground. Jumping over the six-foot bar thus involves lifting his center of gravity only about two feet and then rotating to the horizontal to get over the bar. If he can lift his center of gravity only two feet on Earth, he could lift it 12 feet on the Moon. The highest bar which he could clear on the Moon would be about 16 feet above the surface.

As was noted in Chapter 1, the force of gravity at the surface of the Earth gives freely falling objects an acceleration of 32.2 feet per second per second. Newton's formula $f = ma$, equation (7), shows that if the mass is constant, the acceleration produced by a given force is directly proportional to the force. To illustrate this principle, multiply both members of the equation by two, obtaining $2f = m(2a)$. That is, if we double the force, we produce double the acceleration. Moving an object from Earth to the Moon will not change its mass, but its weight, produced by the force of gravity, is changed. The force of gravity on the Moon is one-sixth as great as on the Earth, and the acceleration it will produce will be $\frac{32.2}{6}$, or about 5.4 feet per second per second.

Before taking the next group of *space flights*, you may find it helpful to quickly review Chapter 1.

Space Flights

3-33. By computation similar to that done above for the Moon, show that the surface gravity on Mars is .39 times the surface gravity on Earth and that the acceleration produced by gravity at the surface of Mars is 12.6 feet per second per second.

3-34. Find the acceleration produced by gravity on each of the planets.

3-35. Verify that the surface gravity given in the table on page 47 for Saturn is correct.

3-36. What velocity would an object reach if it fell freely for 10 seconds on the Moon? On Mars? On Neptune? On Jupiter?

3-37. Through what distance would an object fall in one minute on the Moon? On Mars? On Neptune?

3-38. If a high jumper can clear a bar six feet above the Earth, what height could he clear on Mars? On Neptune? On Jupiter?

3-39. If a man carried a load weighing 100 pounds on Earth up a flight of stairs through a vertical distance of 20 feet, he would do 100×20 or 2,000 foot-pounds of work. How much work would he do in carrying the same object up a similar stairs on the Moon? On Mars? On Saturn? On Venus?

3-40. On June 7, 1963 Brian Sternberg set a collegiate pole vault record of 16 feet 8 inches. How high should he be able to pole vault on the Moon? On Jupiter?

3-41. How much weight would a man need to be able to lift to carry his bride weighing 110 Earth pounds across the threshold on Neptune?

3-42. If he exerted the same effort required on Neptune, how much weight could he carry across a threshold on the Moon?

3-43. According to the 1964 *World Almanac*, the recognized world's record of seven feet five and one-half-inches in the running high jump was set in 1962 by Valery Brumel of the USSR. How high could he jump on the Moon? On Venus?

If a trip by a spacecraft were being planned to the Moon, it would be very important to know the location of the "neutral" point between Earth and the Moon at which the gravitational pulls are equal. A spacecraft leaving the Earth for the Moon along a gravitational orbit would travel at a steadily decreasing velocity until it reached this neutral point. Beyond this point, the gravitational attraction of the Moon would become greater than the attraction of the Earth, and the spacecraft would pick up speed as it approached the Moon.

Suppose that a unit mass is placed at the point P, distance d from the center of the Moon, as shown in Figure 3-4. Since the distance from the center of the Earth to the center of the Moon is 239,000 miles, the distance of P from the center of the Earth will be $239,000 - d$. If M is the mass of the Earth, the gravitational pull F_e of the Earth on the unit mass will be

$$F_e = \frac{G\,M\,(1)}{(239,000 - d)^2}.$$

We know from the table on page 47 that the mass of the Moon is approximately $.012M$, which for convenience we shall express as $\frac{M}{83}$. Thus the gravitational pull F_m of the Moon on the unit mass will be

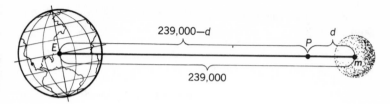

Fig. 3-4

$$F_m = \frac{G\dfrac{M}{83}(1)}{d^2} = \frac{GM(1)}{83d^2}.$$

Since at the neutral point the two gravitational pulls are equal, $F_e = F_m$, and

$$\frac{GM(1)}{(239{,}000 - d)^2} = \frac{GM(1)}{83d^2}.$$

Simplifying,

$$83d^2 = (239{,}000 - d)^2$$
$$d\sqrt{83} = 239{,}000 - d$$
$$d + d\sqrt{83} = 239{,}000$$
$$d(1 + \sqrt{83}) = 239{,}000$$
$$d = \frac{239{,}000}{1 + \sqrt{83}} = \text{approximately } \frac{239{,}000}{1 + 9} = \frac{239{,}000}{10} = 23{,}900.$$

Therefore the neutral point is about 23,900 miles from the Moon, at a point almost precisely nine-tenths of the distance to the Moon.

Space Flights

3-44. The table on page 47 gives the distance to the Sun as 93,000,000 miles, while the mass of the Sun is about 330,000 times the mass of the Earth. Use this data to find the location of the neutral gravitational point between the Earth and Sun.

3-45. In August, 1971, Mars will be about 35,000,000 miles from the Earth. Locate the neutral point between them at that distance.

3-46. Locate the neutral point between Neptune and the Sun.

Source of Energy in the Sun

The Sun is the source of power for the Solar System. The Sun is like a giant furnace producing heat and light. Yet the Sun is in no way like an ordinary furnace which burns chemical fuel. If the Sun obtained its energy by the ordinary chemical burning of fuel, it would have burned up and disappeared several billion years ago. The secret of the Sun's source of heat is found in Einstein's famous equation

$$E = mc^2, \tag{19}$$

in which E is the energy released by the annihilation of a mass m of matter. The value c in the equation is the velocity of light.

The above formula is, of course, the one which is most basic to nuclear science. It expresses the equivalence between matter and energy and infers that either can be transformed into the other. We have not found a way to annihilate matter, but we have found a way to rearrange the nucleus of certain atoms to produce a change in mass. When the nucleus of a heavy element like plutonium is split, lighter elements are formed, and the total mass of the pieces is less than that of the original nucleus. This loss in mass produces energy, and is the basis of the atomic bomb. When nuclei of a light element like hydrogen are fused, heavier elements are formed, and again there is a loss in mass. This loss in mass produces energy, and is the secret of the thermonuclear bomb.

The suns or stars are giant thermonuclear furnaces. At the high temperatures existing in the interiors of the stars, two protons collide with such energy that they form an atom of deuterium, or heavy hydrogen. This atom becomes an atom of ordinary helium by capturing two more protons. Four protons, weighing 4.032 on the atomic weight scale, become a helium atom weighing only 4.004, resulting in a loss in weight of 0.028. This tiny loss of mass becomes energy and is the source of the heat and light from the Sun. Thus the Sun is slowly eating itself up. It has been estimated that at its present rate of hydrogen consumption, the Sun uses up about one percent of its mass in a billion years. Long before our Sun disappears, leaving Earth cold and uninhabitable, our descendents should have found ways of migrating to other star systems or galaxies.

The Universe

Our Solar System, vast as it seems, is an almost infinitesimal speck in a large group of stars called a galaxy. Our Galaxy is shaped like a flattened disk. The part of it that we can see at night is the band of stars overhead called the Milky Way. Our Galaxy is composed of stars and interstellar material. The stars in general follow orbits about the center of the Galaxy. Our Sun lies about eight kiloparsecs from the center of the Galaxy and about four kiloparsecs from the outer edge. It takes our Sun about 250,000,000 years to complete one circuit about the center. The diameter of our Galaxy is about 25 kiloparsecs.

About half of the stars in our Galaxy move through space in pairs. There are other groups containing larger numbers of stars, in addition to many large "globular clusters" each containing at many as 100,000 stars. The interstellar space, although a high vacuum, contains as much material in the form of dust and gas as is found in the stars themselves. Beyond our Galaxy are other galaxies, some of which exist in clusters. There is some evidence that there are super galaxies, each containing hundreds of thousands of galaxies. Obviously the vastness of space is so great that the mind of man can scarcely comprehend it.

The distances to the closer stars are measured by means of parallax. This term was defined in Chapter 2. Astronomers take photographs of stars at half-year intervals, thus using positions which, with reference to the position of the star, are separated by the diameter of the Earth's orbit around the Sun. In Figure 3-6, S is the position of the Sun, r is the radius of the orbit of the Earth, and A and B are positions from which

Fig. 3-5.   The Andromeda Constellation. (NASA)

photographs would be taken. The changes in position of a nearer star as seen against the background of more remote stars may be sufficient to determine the parallax. (The relative distances are exaggerated in Figure 3-6.) When we speak of the parallax of a star, we usually mean the heliocentric parallax, which is half of the greatest parallax observed. After the parallax has been measured, the distance to the star can be calculated.

Reviewing the definition of parsec given in Chapter 2, we recall that a parsec is the distance that corresponds to a parallax of one second of arc. If the angle of parallax is one second ($\frac{1}{3600}$ degree), the distance to the star is one parsec. If the angle of parallax is $\frac{1}{2}$ second of arc, the star is obviously farther away, and the distance is two parsecs. We conclude

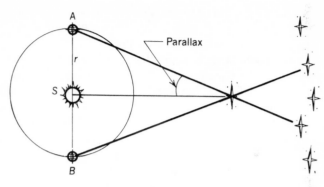

Fig. 3-6

that the distance in parsecs is equal to the reciprocal of the parallax in seconds of arc. Therefore when the parallax p is measured in seconds, indicated by p'',

$$\text{Distance in parsecs} = \frac{1}{p''}. \qquad (20)$$

After we have found the distance in parsecs, we can readily find the distance in light years, astronautical units, or miles by multiplying by the proper factor. These terms were defined in Chapter 2. Remember that one parsec equals 3.26 light years, 206,265 A.U., or 1.92×10^{13} miles.

The parallax of Altair, a star in our Galaxy, is 0.2. Using formula (20), we find that the distance in parsecs is $\frac{1}{0.2}$ or 5. The distance in light years is 5×3.26 or approximately 16. The distance in A.U. is $5 \times 206,265$, or approximately 1,000,000, while the distance in miles is $5 \times 1.92 \times 10^{13}$, or approximately $10 \times 10^{13} = 10^{14}$ miles.

Space Flights

3-47. Find the diameter of our Galaxy in light years. In miles.

3-48. Find the distance from our Sun to the center of our Galaxy in parsecs. In light years. In miles.

3-49. One of the stars nearest the Earth is the bright double star Alpha Centauri. Its parallax is .76 seconds. Find its distance in parsecs. In light years. In miles.

3-50. What would be the parallax of a star that is twice as far away as Alpha Centauri?

3-51. The parallax of Betelgeuse is .005. Find its distance in parsecs. In light years. In miles.

3-52. The distance to Vega is 8.1 parsecs. Find its parallax.

3-53. The distance to Sirius is 8.6 light years. Find its parallax.

3-54. Most persons are able to identify, by its position with relation to the "pointers" in the Big Dipper, the pole star, Polaris. It is 465 light years away. Find its distance in parsecs. Find its parallax.

3-55. Some of the matter in distant galaxies is said to be so dense that on Earth it would weigh 40 tons per cubic inch. Suppose that a man were able to obtain enough of this material so that a stone for the engagement ring of his fiancee could be cut from it. Let us make the setting a cube which measures $\frac{1}{20}$ inch on one edge. Would she be able to wear the ring? What would the setting weigh?

4

Launch Vehicles

Injection into Orbit

Let us consider some of the mathematics involved in placing a body into orbit. As those who have followed the developments in the space age know, bodies are pushed into orbit through the use of rockets or "boosters." A simple rocket consists of a single stage, having one rocket body or framework and a single motor. As we shall see later, present fuels and rocket technology make it generally impossible for single-stage rockets to attain the velocities needed to place satellites into orbit. Rockets with two or more stages are usually used. A multiple-stage rocket is an assembly of several rockets connected in tandem and fired in order. As each stage burns out, it falls away. The satellite is placed at the top of the final stage, and separates from the final stage after orbital velocity has been reached. The velocities needed to achieved orbits, the types of orbit, what keeps a body in orbit, and related topics will be discussed in Chapter 5. A typical satellite launching by a three-stage rocket is represented in Figure 4-1.

As the figure indicates, take-off is vertical or nearly vertical. After the first stage of the rocket has burned out, it separates from the vehicle and falls back to Earth. Since launch is usually over the ocean, the first stage will either fall into the ocean or, if it reached a sufficiently high altitude, be burned up in the Earth's atmosphere as it falls. Similarly, the second stage after burn-out will separate and fall back to Earth. When orbital velocity has been reached, the third stage separates, and the satellite continues on in orbit. The separation of the satellite from the third stage is achieved by the firing of solid-fuel rocket motors or by the releasing of strong springs which give the satellite a little extra push. The satellite will likely achieve a velocity slightly greater than that of the third stage, and will go into a higher orbit. The third stage, however, also has achieved orbital velocity, and will go into an orbit a little lower than that of the satellite. (It is possible that after separation the third stage will still contain a small amount of unburned propellant. In this event, the third stage may reach a velocity greater than that of the satellite and thereby go into a higher orbit.)

Thrust

The force that pushes a rocket, or launch vehicle, into the air is *thrust*. Every person who has played with a toy balloon or has held in his hands a garden hose while watering the lawn has observed the effects of thrust. If we blow up a balloon, as indicated in Figure 4-3, but keep the neck of the

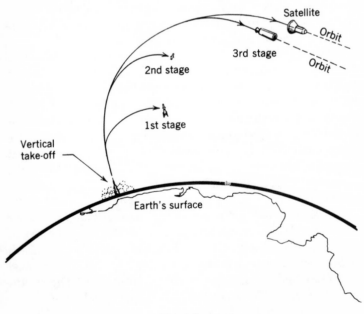

Fig. 4-1

Fig. 4-2. Saturn I boosts a spacecraft into orbit. (NASA)

balloon pinched or tied shut, we have an internal gas pressure in the balloon. But the pressure acts equally against all interior surfaces of the balloon, and therefore it produces no motion. If, however, we let the gas escape from the open end of the balloon, we have an unbalanced pressure within the balloon. There is less pressure near the opening, since the gas is

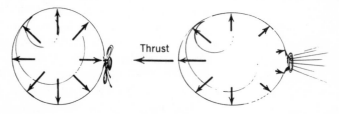

Fig. 4-3

escaping, and the balloon will move in the direction of maximum pressure, away from the opening. Similarly, if water is escaping from a garden hose or a fire hose, there is an unbalanced force resulting from the releasing of the pressure in the hose through the nozzle. The hose will tend to move away from the nozzle. In the case of a fire hose, the thrust produced is sometimes so great that the strength of four or five men may be required to control the hose and the direction of the jet of escaping water. If a chemical fuel and an oxidizer are introduced into a combustion chamber and made to burn, the hot gases produced from the combustion create a high pressure in the chamber. If the exhaust gases are directed to escape through a nozzle at the end of the chamber, an unbalanced force is again produced pushing the chamber in a direction opposite that of the escaping gases.

The thrust produced by a jet is an illustration of Newton's Third Law of Motion, which states that for each force action there is an equal and opposite reaction. Many persons have thought that the thrust produced by a jet is a result of the pushing of the molecules in the jet against the molecules in the surrounding air. The jet, however, produces thrust equally well in a vacuum where there are no molecules of air. In fact, a jet is more effective in a vacuum than it is in air for two reasons: there is no air drag to retard the motion of the moving body; and the exhaust jet expands more readily in a vacuum. An exhaust jet is 10 to 20 percent more effective in a vacuum than in air.

The design and behavior of rocket engines and exhaust nozzles involves physical and chemical principles and related mathematical applications which are beyond the scope of this book. It is possible for us to discuss the application of mathematics to simple basic principles only. Figure 4-4 pictures a combustion chamber and exhaust nozzle. Fuel with an oxidizer is introduced into the combustion chamber A and made to burn there. The hot exhaust gases flow toward the nozzle and are exhausted into the atmosphere. The internal pressure is much less at the nozzle end than it is in the combustion chamber, as is indicated by the relative lengths of the arrows.

This unbalanced force produces a thrust away from the nozzle, as indicated. The nozzle has a curved inner surface which narrows at the throat B and then widens at C. This is not the only shape used for nozzles, but this particular design has proved to be efficient. The purpose of the constriction at B is to accelerate the exhaust gases as they leave the combustion chamber. Making them pass through a smaller opening increases their velocity at that point. The nozzle then widens so that the high-velocity exhaust gases expand rapidly until they are reduced to atmospheric pressure. During this expansion process the gases gain additional velocity.

In a perfectly designed nozzle the exhaust gases have expanded to atmospheric pressure when they reach the exit point C. If P_e is the pressure of the exhaust gases at point C, P_a is the ambient pressure (the pressure of the surrounding atmosphere), and A_e is the area of the nozzle exit, then the efficiency of the nozzle is represented by the expression $(P_e - P_a)\ A_e$. If $P_e < P_a$, the value of $(P_e - P_a)\ A_e < 0$, and there is a loss in thrust. It would seem that the nozzle should be designed so that $P_e > P_a$. In this case, however, a "balling up" of gases, or a pressure block behind the nozzle, may interfere with the escape of the remaining gases. Ideally $P_e = P_a$, so that $(P_e - P_a)\ A_e = 0$. When we consider that P_a, the ambient pressure, will vary from 14.7 to zero pounds per square inch as the booster rises, it becomes obvious that a simple equation

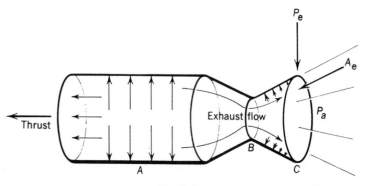

Fig. 4-4

is inadequate to explain the design and operation of nozzles. The nozzle engineer depends a great deal upon experimentation in finding the optimum design for a nozzle.

The thrust produced by a chemical rocket is dependent upon the rate of burning of the propellant fuel, the velocity of the exhaust gases, and the propellant burning time. Under ideal conditions these quantities are related by the equation

$$f = \frac{w}{t\,g}c, \qquad (21)$$

in which w is the total weight in pounds of the propellant burned, t is the propellant burning time in seconds, c is the ideal (or maximum) exhaust velocity in feet per second, g is the acceleration of gravity in feet per second per second, and f is the thrust in pounds. The actual thrust is given more accurately if we add the quantity derived above to measure the efficiency of the nozzle. Thus we obtain the more complete equation,

$$f = \frac{w}{t\,g}c + (P_e - P_a)\,A_e. \qquad (22)$$

Suppose that a small rocket engine burns 18 pounds of propellant per second for a total burning time of six seconds, giving an exhaust velocity 3000 feet per second. Assume that $P_e = 10$ pounds per square inch. The nozzle exit area is eight square inches. The thrust produced at sea level is then

$$f = \frac{108}{6 \times 32.2} \times 3000 + (10 - 14.7) \times 8 = 1677 - 38$$
$$= 1639 \text{ pounds.}$$

The theoretical thrust when the rocket reaches an altitude where the atmospheric pressure is 10 pounds per square inch is $1677 + (10 - 10) \times 8 = 1677 + 0 = 1677$ pounds. The rocket engine becomes more efficient when it reaches higher altitudes.

Space Flights

4-1. Assume that the internal pressure in a small balloon is 16 pounds per square inch. The opening or orifice through which the air escapes has an area of $\frac{1}{20}$ square inch. What is the thrust in ounces that makes the balloon move?

4-2. A rocket uses propellant at the rate of 25 pounds per second. The exit pressure is 15 pounds per square inch, the exit velocity of the gases is 5000 feet per second, and the nozzle exit area is 10 square inches. What thrust does the rocket develop at sea level? At an altitude of $3\frac{1}{4}$ miles?

4-3. A rocket develops a thrust of 8000 pounds at an altitude of 20,000 feet. The exit velocity of the exhaust is 6000 feet per second, the nozzle exit pressure is 12 pounds per square inch, and the nozzle exit area is 12 square inches. Find the rate of use of propellant.

4-4. A rocket with an ideal nozzle, in which $P_e = P_a$, burns 18 pounds of propellant per second for a total burning time of two seconds, producing a thrust of 2000 pounds. What is the velocity of the exhaust?

Velocity and Altitude

The thrust produced by a rocket engine moves the vehicle from its stationary position and gives it an acceleration. The acceleration produced can be calculated by equation (9), $a = \dfrac{f\,g}{w}$, in which f is the thrust measured in pounds and w is the total weight being lifted. The velocity produced by this acceleration during a given interval of time is given by equation (2), $v = at$. A little reflection will soon convince us that the application of these simple equations has limited practical value in a process as complicated as the launching of a satellite. In order that the exhaust gases have sufficient velocity, it is necessary that the fuel burn very rapidly, and many tons of fuel will be burned within a few minutes. The thrust may remain relatively constant during a short interval, but the weight being lifted is rapidly decreasing, resulting in a rapidly increasing acceleration. Initially there will be a large atmospheric drag as the vehicle moves with increasing velocity through the dense lower atmosphere. By the time the first stage separates, the vehicle may be above most of the Earth's atmosphere, and air resistance becomes negligible. The rocket engines become more efficient in the rarefied atmosphere, and the thrust increases. Furthermore the retarding effect of gravity becomes less as the vehicle gets far above the surface of the Earth.

Thus the formula, $a = \dfrac{f \, g}{w}$, which involves constant quantities only, has little direct use in a situation in which all quantities are changing. The application of this formula to some simple single-stage rockets, however, will help to clarify understandings. If we base our computations on *average* values, the results obtained agree remarkably well with actual experience.

If a rocket is to be lifted vertically, it is obvious that the thrust measured in pounds must be greater than the total take-off weight of the rocket. If the thrust were just equal to the weight, it would be capable only of counteracting the force of gravity. It could balance the weight of the vehicle, but it could not lift it. We are interested in the concept known as the *thrust-to-weight ratio*. This is the ratio of the thrust to the total loaded weight of the rocket. If the ratio is one or less than one, the rocket cannot be lifted from the ground. The thrust-to-weight ratio varies in practical applications from about 1.25 to 3. The ratio changes of course during launch as the load of propellant is reduced by burning.

Since the thrust must lift the weight of the rocket before it can push it from the ground, we must modify formula (9) by subtracting the weight w from f to obtain

$$a = \frac{(f - w) \, g}{w}$$

or
$$a = g \left(\frac{f}{w} - 1 \right). \tag{23}$$

This formula gives us the acceleration that will be produced by the thrust remaining after the pull of gravity has been overcome. Note that $\dfrac{f}{w}$ is the thrust-to-weight ratio. In order to investigate further this formula, assume that it is possible to have a rocket in which there is a nearly constant thrust-to-weight ratio of 1.5. The acceleration a is easily found as follows:

$$a = 32.2 \ (1.5 - 1) = 32.2 \ (.5) = 16.1 \text{ feet per second}$$
$$\text{per second.}$$

Assume that the supply of propellant burns out, ending the thrust, in 10 seconds. The altitude that the rocket will reach in that time is easily found from formula (4):

$$s = \frac{1}{2} \ (16.1)(10^2) = 850 \text{ feet.}$$

The velocity reached will be, by formula (2),

$$v = (16.1)(10) = 161 \text{ feet per second.}$$

The rocket, however, will not stop immediately. It will continue to rise under its own inertia, but at a steadily decreasing velocity as the pull of gravity slows it down, until it completely stops and begins to fall back to Earth. The additional distance that its burn-out velocity of 161 feet per second will carry it can be found from equation (5). Since there is now no more thrust to move the rocket, the force which controls the remainder of the flight will be gravity. When a body is acting under the acceleration of gravity, we usually think of a downward movement. In this case the movement is up, but it is the downward trip in reverse, and the same equation applies. Substituting g for a in equation (5), we obtain

$$s = \frac{v^2}{2g}. \qquad (24)$$

Since $v = 161$, $\qquad s = \dfrac{161^2}{2 \times 32.2} = 402.5.$

That is, the additional distance the rocket rises after burn-out will be 402.5 feet. The total height reached by the rocket is $805 + 402.5 = 1207.5$, or about 1208 feet.

The preceding computation enables us to write at once a fundamental formula in missiles and rocketry giving the maximum height a rocket can attain. Let H be the maximum height, while h is the height at burn-out, and v is the velocity attained at burn-out. The maximum height is clearly the height at burn-out plus the additional height to which the rocket will "coast" under its own inertia. The total height is therefore

$$H = h + \frac{v^2}{2g}. \qquad (25)$$

This formula assumes that the rocket has been launched vertically.

Space Flights

4-5. Find the height at burn-out, the velocity at burn-out, and the total height for the above rocket if the thrust is effective for 30 seconds.

4-6. The behavior of the above rocket probably would agree more closely with experience if we assume that about 80 percent of the take-off weight is propellant being burned at a steady rate. If the total initial weight of the rocket were 10 pounds, the weight at burn-out would be two pounds, and the average weight would be six pounds. If the take-off thrust-to-weight ratio were 1.5, then the thrust was evidently 15 pounds, giving an *average* thrust-to-weight ratio of $\frac{15}{6}$ or 2½. Find the height and velocity at burn-out and the total height for burning times of 10 seconds and 30 seconds. Compare your results with those previously obtained.

4-7. What does equation (23) tell about the behavior of a rocket if $f = w$? If $f < w$?

4-8. A small rocket has a weight of six ounces, and 80 percent is propellant. It has a thrust of 30 ounces lasting for 2 seconds. Using the average weight, find the maximum height that it will reach? The maximum velocity?

4-9. A booster has a thrust of 90,000 pounds and a take-off weight of 20 tons. Find the thrust-to-weight ratio.

4-10. The German V-2 rocket had a total weight of 28,000 pounds and a thrust of 56,000 pounds. Find its thrust-to-weight ratio.

4-11. A rocket has an average thrust-to-weight ratio of two. For how many seconds must the propellant fuel burn in order that the altitude at burn-out will be 2500 feet?

4-12. One of the early space boosters developed by the United States was Vanguard. Its total take-off weight was 22,000 pounds, while the thrust of its first stage was 27,000 pounds. Find its thrust-to-weight ratio at take-off.

4-13. One of the early antiaircraft missiles had the following specifications: take-off dry weight 4200 pounds, fuel 4200 pounds (giving an average "in-flight" weight of 6300 pounds), thrust 17,500 pounds, and burning time 45 seconds. Find its velocity and altitude at burn-out.

4-14. The first stage of the launch vehicle Saturn V will be powered by five Rocketdyne engines each generating about 1.5 million pounds of thrust. The total weight of the first stage at take-off will be 2350 tons. The second stage will weigh 500 tons at take-off, and the third stage will weigh 125 tons. It will lift a payload of 45 tons. Find the thrust-to-weight ratio of the entire vehicle at take-off.

4-15. If we multiply both members of the equation $a = g\left(\dfrac{f}{w} - 1\right)$ by t, the burning time, we obtain an equation giving directly the burn-out velocity, since $v = at$. Remove parentheses in the right member and identify the expression giving the reduction in velocity caused by the pull of gravity.

Specific Impulse

If equation (21) for thrust is solved for $\dfrac{c}{g}$, we obtain

$$\frac{f\,t}{w} = \frac{c}{g}.$$

The quantity $\dfrac{f\,t}{w}$ is called the specific impulse. If we represent specific impulse by I_s, we have

$$I_s = \frac{f\,t}{w} = \frac{f}{w/t}. \tag{26}$$

Since w is the total amount in pounds of propellant burned, while t is the burning time in seconds, the quantity $\dfrac{w}{t}$ represents the rate at which propellant is burned in terms of number of pounds per second. Specific impulse, I_s, is therefore the ratio of the thrust produced to the rate of use of propellant. It has the same general meaning to a rocket engineer that miles per gallon has to the driver of an automobile. Since the ratio $\dfrac{f}{w/t}$ involves pounds in the numerator divided by pounds in the denominator, the pounds divide out leaving the answer in seconds. If a propellant, for example, has a specific impulse of 300 seconds, the burning of one pound of the propellant will (1) produce a thrust of 300 pounds if burned in one second, or (2) produce a thrust of one pound lasting through a burning time of 300 seconds.

It is apparent from equation (21) that specific impulse can also be expressed in the form

$$I_s = \frac{c}{g}. \tag{27}$$

With this form of the equation we can find the maximum exhaust velocity produced by a propellant if we know its specific impulse, and vice versa.

We noted in *space flight* 4-10 above that the German V-2 rocket had a thrust of 56,000 pounds. It consumed about 18,000 pounds of propellant in a burning time of 64 seconds. Its specific impulse is found by equation (26) to be $I_s = \dfrac{56,000 \times 64}{18,000} = 200$ seconds. This is a relatively low specific impulse as compared with those realized from modern propellants. If we use the second form (27) of the specific impulse equation, we can compute the effective exhaust velocity for the V-2. Evidently $c = gI_s = 32.2 \times 200 = 6440$ feet per second.

Modern rockets and launch vehicles depend on chemical propellants, and the highest specific impulses have been obtained from liquid propellants. Liquid propellants have a further advantage in that a motor using them can be stopped and restarted while in flight. For ease of handling and storage, solid propellants are convenient. However the specific impulses provided by the best solid propellants are still well below those available from the best liquid propellants. Rocket motors with solid propellants cannot be stopped and restarted in flight. Following is a group of typical chemical propellants with the specific impulses they provide. The figures given in the table are those the author has found in publications by various authorities in this field. They may not be in close agreement in all cases with the specific impulses given by others. The list is, of course, far from complete, and it only suggests the types of present chemical propellants. It is probable that a specific impulse of about 400 seconds represents the maximum that can be attained with chemical fuels.

Propellant	Specific Impulse in Seconds
Liquid oxygen and refined kerosene	286
Liquid oxygen and liquid hydrogen	388
Fluorine and liquid hydrogen	398
Nitric acid and refined kerosene	258
Typical solid propellant	230

Following are specific impulses for other types of propulsion systems not yet operational but which may be perfected in the future. Although the specific impulses of some of these systems are high, giving high exhaust velocities, the rate of emission of particles is low, producing low thrust. As we shall see in Chapter 6, such low-thrust systems might be useful for space trips after the spacecraft has been placed in orbit by other means.

Propulsion System	Specific Impulse in Seconds
Nuclear propulsion	800 to 1,000
Arc jet	800 to 1,500
Ion propulsion	3,500 to 15,000

Total Impulse

Total impulse is specific impulse multiplied by the total weight of the propellant used. If total impulse is represented by I_t, then

$$I_t = I_s w, \qquad (28)$$

where w is the weight of propellant in pounds. Total impulse is therefore measured in pound-seconds. Total impulse is useful in comparing the size of rocket vehicles. For example, if two rockets use propellants with the same specific impulses, and the first has twice the total impulse of the second, then the first rocket obviously burns twice as much propellant as the second one, and is capable of greater performance.

Since $I_s = \dfrac{f\,t}{w}$, we may rewrite equation (28) in the form $I_t = \dfrac{f\,t}{w}\,w$, obtaining the equation

$$I_t = ft. \qquad (29)$$

That is, the total impulse of a rocket is equal to the thrust in pounds multiplied by the burning time in seconds. Having a high total impulse would be especially important for long space trips. The total impulse might be utilized in either of two ways: (1) to produce a high thrust with a short burning time or (2) a low thrust with a long burning time. The ways in which these two possibilities may be utilized on long space trips will be discussed in Chapter 6.

Space Flights

4-16. Compute the maximum exhaust velocity for each of the propellants or propulsion systems listed above.

4-17. Three low-thrust control rockets are used in the launching of a satellite to push the capsule away after separation from the final stage of the booster. Each rocket uses six pounds of solid propellant with a specific impulse of 225 seconds and a burning time of 1.5 seconds. What is the thrust produced by each rocket?

4-18. Find the total impulse of each control rocket above.

4-19. A rocket burns 100 tons of liquid oxygen and kerosene (specific impulse 286 seconds). What is the total impulse? What is the thrust produced if the fuel is burned in five minutes? In five months?

4-20. A low-thrust control rocket produces a thrust of five pounds by burning in 0.3 seconds a quantity of solid propellant with specific impulse 225 seconds. How many pounds of propellant are used?

4-21. *Space flight* 4-13 gave data on an antiaircraft missile. Substitute the appropriate quantities in formula (26) to find the specific impulse of the propellant.

4-22. The Aerobee-Hi rocket had a dry weight of 234 pounds, a propellant load of 888 pounds, and developed a thrust of 4,100 pounds during a burning time of 42 seconds. Find the specific impulse of the propellant.

4-23. What was the total impulse of the Aerobee-Hi rocket described above?

4-24. The Saturn I is a two-stage rocket with the following specifications. The first stage burns 425 tons of liquid oxygen and kerosene (specific impulse 286) to produce a thrust of 1,500,000 pounds. The second stage burns 50 tons of liquid oxygen and liquid hydrogen (specific impulse 388) to produce a thrust of 90,000 pounds. Find the burning time of each stage and the total burning time of the rocket.

4-25. The Saturn V, the booster being developed to place astronauts on the Moon, is a three-stage rocket with these specifications. The first stage will burn 2200 tons of propellant with a specific impulse of 286 producing 7,500,000 pounds of thrust. The second stage will burn 456 tons of propellant with specific impulse 388 to produce 1,000,000 pounds of thrust. The third stage will have a thrust of 200,000 pounds by burning 115 tons of propellant with specific impulse 388. Find the burning time of each stage and the total burning time of the booster.

4-26. Find the total impulse of the Saturn V.

Maximum Velocity of a Rocket

What is the maximum velocity a rocket can attain? The theoretical maximum velocity of any rocket, its velocity at burn-out, is given by a rather simple equation,

$$v = c \log_e R, \tag{30}$$

in which v and c are the maximum velocities of the rocket and the exhaust respectively. R, the *mass ratio*, is the ratio of the fully loaded take-off weight of the rocket to the empty or dry weight. Suppose that an empty rocket weighs 9,000 pounds, its payload weighs 1,000 pounds, and its full load of propellant weighs 20,000 pounds. Then the weight fully loaded is $9,000 + 1,000 + 20,000 = 30,000$. Its empty weight, before the propellant is loaded, is $9,000 + 1,000 = 10,000$. The mass ratio R is $\frac{30,000}{10,000} = 3$.

Use equation (30) to find the maximum velocity (at burnout) of the V-2 rocket. We were given the information in a previous discussion that its take-off weight was 28,000 pounds. It consumed about 18,000 pounds of propellant, giving an empty weight of $28,000 - 18,000$ pounds. Its mass ratio R was therefore $\frac{28,000}{10,000} = 2.8$. We found that its maximum exhaust velocity c was 6440 feet per second. Its maximum velocity is therefore $v = 6440 \log_e 2.8 = 6440 \times 1.03 = 6633$ feet per second or about 4,520 miles per hour. (We find the value of $\log_e 2.8$ by referring to the table of natural logarithms in the Appendix. Remember that the logarithm of a number is the exponent to which some base must be raised to get that number. Thus the equation $\log_b x = y$ says that y is the exponent to which the base b must be raised to get x, and can be written in the alternate form $b^y = x$. The base of natural logarithms is the number e, which is approximately equal to 2.72.)

Equation (30) for the maximum velocity of a rocket makes it clear that there are two chief ways to improve the performance of a rocket. (1) We may increase the exhaust velocity c by using a propellant with a higher specific impulse. (2) We may increase the mass ratio R. The mass ratio can be increased only by devoting a larger portion of the total loaded weight of the rocket to propellant. Study the effect of these possibilities upon the performance of the Viking rocket.

Published data tells us that the exhaust velocity of the Viking was about 1.2 miles per second, while the weight breakdown was: propellant 80 percent, structure 15 percent, payload 5 percent. The mass ratio was therefore $\frac{100}{15+5} = \frac{100}{20} = 5$. The maximum velocity was $v = 1.2 \times \log_e 5 = 1.21 \times 1.61 = 1.93$ miles per second. The specific impulse of the propellant used in the Viking was nearly 200 seconds. Suppose we are able to find a new chemical propellant with the theoretical maximum specific impulse of 400 seconds. The maximum velocities of the exhaust and the rocket would both be doubled, increasing to 2.4 and 3.86 miles per second respectively.

Let us assume for the moment, however, that we wish to use the doubled specific impulse not to increase the burn-out velocity but to permit a redistribution of the weight. We have with our new exhaust velocity of 2.4,

$$1.93 = 2.4 \log_e R$$
$$\log_e R = 0.8.$$

We find from a table of logarithms that $R = 2.24$, meaning that the mass ratio can be reduced to 2.24 instead of 5 as before. We can obtain the same performance with a mass ratio less than half as large as before. We now anticipate a smaller propellant load, so that the structure will not need to be as strong as before. Therefore, assign 10 of the 100 parts to structure and p parts to payload. Then, since $R = 2.24$,

$$\frac{100}{10 + p} = 2.24$$
$$100 = 10 \times 2.24 + 2.24p$$
$$2.24p = 77.6$$
$$p = 34.6 \text{ or approximately 35.}$$

The payload has now been multiplied by seven, and the propellant needed is only 55 percent of the total weight. Doubling the specific impulse would enable us to replace 25 parts of propellant by payload, increasing considerably the usefulness of the rocket without sacrificing performance. We now have two choices resulting from doubling the specific impulse, a 5 percent payload with a maximum velocity of

3.86 miles per second or a 35 percent payload with a maximum velocity of 1.93 miles per second. Neither velocity will place the payload into orbit.

Let us experiment with the second possibility of increasing the maximum velocity by increasing the mass ratio. If we reduce the weight of the structure too much, the rocket may become too fragile to stand the stresses of operation. Therefore, reduce the weight of the payload to one percent of the total weight and the weight of the structure to five percent, using 94 percent of the total weight for propellant. The mass ratio is now $\frac{94}{6} = 15.7$. Then

$$v = 1.2 \times \log_e 15.7 = 1.2 \times 2.75 = 3.30 \text{ miles per second.}$$

This higher maximum velocity, which we have achieved by making the payload so small that the flight is scarcely worth the effort, is still below orbital velocity. There remains a third possibility. We can increase both the mass ratio and the specific impulse. If we keep the above mass ratio of 15.7 and also double the specific impulse, we obtain a maximum velocity of 6.6 miles per second. As we shall find in Chapter 5, this velocity is greater than that required for placing an object into a circular orbit but much less than escape velocity. This velocity would be considerably reduced by the losses resulting from the pull of gravity, friction with the atmosphere, and other causes. Whether the remaining "net" velocity would orbit the insignificant one percent payload cannot be known without further information.

The previous discussion, even though it is based upon some arbitrary assumption about a given rocket, points out rather clearly the limitations of single-stage rockets. With the best of modern chemical propellants, single-stage rockets can scarcely put useful payloads even into circular orbits, much less escape orbits. The solution to the problem lies in the use of multiple-stage boosters. The previous discussion also points out rather vividly the great benefits that accrue in the ability of boosters to carry much larger payloads when specific impulses can be increased.

Space Flights

4-27. A rocket has a mass ratio of four. Its propellant, with specific impulse 330, burns out in two minutes. Find its maximum velocity. Assuming a vertical launch, use equation (25) to find the total height to which it will rise.

4-28. A velocity of 17,500 miles per hour is required to place an object in orbit at an altitude of 100 miles. If the propellant has a specific impulse of 300, what mass ratio would be required for placement of a payload into orbit? (Note that we have ignored the retarding forces of gravity and air resistance, so the maximum velocity needed is greater than indicated above.)

Retarding Effect of Gravity

In the previous discussion of the maximum velocity that a rocket can attain, we ignored the reduction in velocity caused by the pull of gravity and friction with the atmosphere. The retarding effect of friction with the atmosphere cannot be given without more information than we have available. The retarding effect of the pull of gravity will depend on the angle of launch. Throughout this book we have assumed that launch is vertical. We know from equation (2) that for a vertical launch the reduction in velocity will be gt. Therefore, our formula for the maximum velocity of a rocket will give more accurate results if written as

$$v = c \log_e R - gt. \qquad (31)$$

Obviously we must know the flight time, the value of t, to use this formula. (Note that the retarding force of gravity was accounted for in the derivation of formula (23). Also your answer to *space flight* 4-15 should have identified gt as the retarding quantity.) In the following exercises assume that the launch is vertical, and base your computation on equation (31).

Space Flights

4-29. Find the maximum velocity (at burn-out) and the corresponding altitude of the antiaircraft missile described in *space flight* 4-13. Compare your result with that previously obtained through the use of equation (23).

4-30. Data for the Aerobee-Hi was given in *space flight* 4-22. Using the specific impulse which you computed, find its velocity and altitude at burn-out and the total altitude which it will reach.

4-31. The Aerobee-Hi was designed to carry a 200-pound payload to a height of 122 miles. Find its velocity and altitude at burn-out and the total altitude it would reach when carrying a payload of 200 pounds.

Multiple-Stage Boosters

Consider the difference between single-stage and multiple stage boosters. A multiple-stage booster has several rockets arranged in tandem. The stages fire in order, and each drops off and falls back toward Earth after burn-out. After the first stage drops off, there will be a short coasting interval, after which the second stage, which now has a high initial velocity, will ignite. The velocity it produces is added to the velocity of the first stage. The burning and dropping away of the heavy first stage greatly increases the mass ratio and gives the remaining part of the booster a "new lease on life." These steps are repeated as each burned-out stage drops away, until the final stage is fired. Since the final velocity is the sum of the individual velocities, the formula for velocity at final burn-out of a three-stage rocket becomes

$$v = c_1 \log_e R_1 + c_2 \log_e R_2 + c_3 \log_e R_3, \tag{32}$$

where the subscripts identify the exhaust velocities and mass ratios of stages one, two, and three respectively. R_1 is the ratio of the weight of the entire booster, including the payload and the propellants in all three stages, to the remaining weight after the propellant in the first stage has burned out. Then the shell for the first stage drops off, so that R_2 is the ratio of the total weight of the remaining parts of the rocket, including propellants and payload, to the weight after the propellant in stage two has burned out, etc. In this formula we have not included a correction for the retarding effect of gravity. It will be noted from Figure 4-1 that for a launch to a high altitude, the retarding effect of gravity may become insignificant after the dropping of the first stage, since the launch may no longer be vertical. In the following problems we shall ignore the retarding effects of gravity and atmospheric drag.

As an example, assume that we have a small three-stage rocket. The first stage weighs 40 pounds dry and holds 50 additional pounds of propellant with a specific impulse of 230 seconds. The comparable weights for the second stage are 22 pounds and 15 pounds, and for the third stage 12 pounds and nine pounds. The propellant in the second and third stages has a specific impulse of 250 seconds. The rocket carries a payload weighing 10 pounds. Then $c_1 = 32.2 \times 230 = 7406$, and $c_2 = c_3 = 32.2 \times 250 = 8050$. We find that

$$R_1 = \frac{40 + 50 + 22 + 15 + 12 + 9 + 10}{40 + 22 + 15 + 12 + 9 + 10} = \frac{158}{108} = 1.46,$$

$$R_2 = \frac{22 + 15 + 12 + 9 + 10}{22 + 12 + 9 + 10} = \frac{68}{53} = 1.28,$$

and $$R_3 = \frac{12 + 9 + 10}{12 + 10} = \frac{31}{22} = 1.41.$$

Therefore

$$v = 7406 \log_e 1.46 + 8050 \log_e 1.28 + 8050 \log_e 1.41$$
$$= 7406 \,(.378) + 8050 \,(.247) + 8050 \,(.344)$$
$$= 2799 + 1988 + 2769 = 7556.$$

The maximum velocity is about 7560 feet per second or 5150 miles per hour.

Space Flights

4-32. A Saturn I booster was launched experimentally by NASA on January 29, 1964. The second stage with its load of ballast weighed 19 tons after burn-out. It was placed in an elliptical orbit with apogee 467 miles and perigee 162 miles. The dry weight of the first stage was 63 tons. Additional data was given in *space flight* 4-24. Find the theoretical maximum velocity of Saturn I. Do your figures indicate that the velocity would be sufficient to place the second stage into orbit?

4-33. The Saturn V is designed to place a payload of 45 tons in orbit about the Moon. The following specifications combined with those given in *space flight* 4-25 should enable you to find the maximum theoretical velocity. The dry weights of the first, second, and third stages are respectively 150 tons, 44 tons, and 10 tons. The payload of 45 tons must, of course, be added to the dry weight of the third stage. Will the theoretical maximum velocity be greater than escape velocity?

5

Bodies in Orbit

How a Body Remains in Orbit

If a ball is thrown into the air or if a bullet or projectile is shot into the air, it will, ignoring air resistance, follow a parabolic path. This was the path followed by the first two manned space flights made by American astronauts. Although the spacecraft were boosted high above the Earth, they were not placed in orbit. The first flight was made on May 4, 1961 by Alan B. Shepard in a Mercury spaceship called *Freedom 7*. The ship was launched to an altitude of 115 miles, and landed in the Atlantic Ocean 302 miles from the launch site after a flight of 15 minutes. *Freedom 7* followed an arc of a parabola, as pictured in Figure 5-1.

The first orbital flight by an American was made by John H. Glenn, Jr. on February 20, 1962. L. Gordon Cooper during his flight on May 15-16, 1963 made 22 orbits around the Earth. The orbits in both of these flights were nearly circular. What are the physical conditions needed to place and keep a body in orbit?

One approach to finding the answer to this question is to consider the behavior of a falling body. Galileo found that all bodies fall toward the Earth at the same rate regardless of their size or weight. Intuitively one would expect a heavy body to fall faster. If air resistance is neglected, however, all bodies behave as Galileo stated. For example, if a coin and a feather are placed in a tube and then the air is pumped out to create a vacuum, both the coin and the feather will fall together if the tube is placed on end.

The distance s in feet which a body will fall in t seconds is

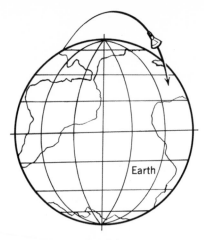

Fig. 5-1

found from formula (4) if we replace a by g, obtaining

$$s = \tfrac{1}{2}\, gt^2$$

where g, the acceleration produced by the attraction of gravity, is 32.2 feet per second during each second. This equation shows that if a body falls freely for a period of 10 seconds, the distance in feet through which it will fall is $s = \tfrac{1}{2}(32.2)(10^2) = 16.1 \times 100 = 1610$.

If we solve the above equation for t, we obtain

$$t = \sqrt{\frac{2\,s}{g}}. \tag{33}$$

This form of the equation is convenient if we wish to find the time required for an object to fall a given distance. The number of seconds needed for an object to fall 100 feet is

$$t = \sqrt{\frac{2 \times 100}{32.2}} = \sqrt{\frac{100}{16.1}} = 2.5.$$

It is interesting to note that an object dropped from a height of 100 feet will reach the ground in precisely the same time that would be required if it were thrown to the side. That is, the vertical and horizontal motions are independent of each

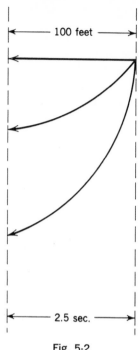

Fig. 5-2

other and do not interfere with each other, as shown in Figure 5-2.

Space Flights

5-1. A stone is dropped from a cliff 50 feet high. In how many seconds will it strike the ground?

5-2. A bullet is fired horizontally from a gun six feet above the ground with a muzzle velocity of 2000 feet per second. After how many seconds will the bullet hit the ground? If the bullet is not slowed by air resistance, how far from the firing point will the landing place be?

5-3. An object falls for five seconds. Find the individual distances covered during each of the five seconds.

5-4. An object is dropped for one mile. How long will it take the object to fall?

Falling Around the Earth

Suppose an object is thrown from a cliff a mile high. The time required for the object to reach the Earth, whether we let it drop straight down or throw it vigorously in a horizontal direction, will be approximately 18.1 seconds, as you found in *space flight* 5-4 above. Throw the object as vigorously as possible in a horizontal direction. Then, because of the curvature of the Earth, the downward distance will be somewhat increased, since the Earth will curve gently away from the horizontal path. If we could throw the object in a horizontal direction with sufficient velocity that the Earth would have curved away one mile while the object fell one mile, then it would appear this motion could be repeated indefinitely, the object remaining, even though continually falling, always one mile above the surface of the Earth. The object would then be in a circular orbit at a distance of one mile high around the Earth.

This situation is pictured in Figure 5-3. The object is thrown at Point A, one mile above the Earth, along the line AB. At the end of 18.1 seconds it has fallen one mile to point C. The Earth, however, because of its curvature, has descended one mile below the horizontal line EC, so that the falling object when it reaches point C is still one mile above the surface of the Earth. What is the horizontal distance EC? To a person standing at A, the point D at which line AD is tangent to the surface of the Earth is clearly the horizon seen from A. Similarly the point E marks the horizon that would be seen from point C. Equation (16) enables us to find the distance to the horizon. Applying this formula, we find that from a point one mile above the Earth the horizon is 88.9 miles away. Thus $AD = EC = 88.9$ miles. The reader will realize that the relative distances in Figure 5-3 must be greatly exaggerated, but the reasonableness of this example would be readily apparent if the figure were drawn to scale.

If the object is to remain in orbit, it must have a horizontal velocity sufficient to carry it a horizontal distance of 88.9 miles in 18.1 seconds. Dividing the distance by the time yields a

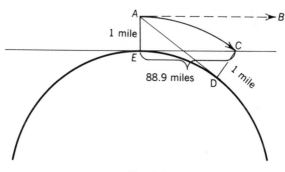

Fig. 5-3

velocity of 4.9 miles per second or 17,600 miles per hour. Although the object is continually falling, it never strikes the Earth. An object in this condition is often said to be in "free fall."

Velocity Required for a Circular Orbit

If we look at the problem of keeping a body in orbit from a slightly different viewpoint, we can derive a general formula enabling the solution to many problems related to orbits. In Chapter 1 we discussed some of the mathematics of circular motion. Equation (10) states that the centripetal force needed to constrain a body to move in a circular path is $F = \dfrac{mv^2}{r}$. The force keeping a satellite in a circular path about the Earth is, of course, the gravitational pull of the Earth. Newton's Law of Universal Gravitation expresses the attraction between a satellite and the Earth in equation (13) as $F = G\dfrac{Mm}{r^2}$. In these equations m is the mass of the satellite, M is the mass of the Earth, G is the constant of universal gravitation, and r is the radius of revolution measured from the center of the Earth. When a satellite is in a stable orbit, the attraction between the satellite and the Earth will exactly equal the centripetal force, so that

$$\frac{m \; v^2}{r} = G \, \frac{Mm}{r^2}.$$

Simplifying, we obtain $v^2 = \dfrac{G \; M}{r}$

and $v = \sqrt{\dfrac{G \; M}{r}}.$ (34)

The values of G and M have been measured many times by physicists. The value of GM, expressed in units of miles and seconds, is 9.56 (10^4). Our formula may be written,

$$v = \sqrt{\frac{9.56 \; (10^4)}{r}}.$$ (35)

With this formula we can readily calculate the velocity to achieve an orbit at a given radius, and conversely. Since the value of the constant GM as given above is expressed in terms of miles and seconds, the values for v and r also must be expressed in these units. The radius r must be given in miles and the corresponding velocity is in miles per second.

Assume that we are to orbit a satellite around the Earth at sea level. We know, of course, that it is impossible for us to orbit an object at sea level since the Earth is not smooth, and the dense atmosphere at sea level would create such a strong "drag" on the satellite that it would soon be slowed to a speed less than orbital velocity. However the theoretical velocity of a "tree top" orbit is of interest, since it indicates the maximum velocity at which an object could orbit the Earth, and it enables us to find later the escape velocity at the surface of the Earth. Since $r = 3960$ miles,

$$v = \sqrt{\frac{9.56 \; (10^4)}{3960}} = \sqrt{24.14} = 4.9 \text{ miles per second.}$$

To obtain the velocity in miles per hour, we must multiply by 3600, the number of seconds in one hour. We find that 4.9 $\times$ 3600 = approximately 17,600 miles per hour, which agrees with the velocity obtained through the informal experiment at the beginning of this chapter.

Period of a Circular Orbit

Find the length of time required for one orbit at sea level. The circumference of the Earth at sea level is $2\pi r = 2\pi(3960)$ $= 6.28 \times 3960 =$ approximately 24,900 miles. The time required for one orbit is $\dfrac{24,900}{17,600} = 1.41$ hours, or 84.6 minutes. It is interesting to note that the actual time interval required for one orbit may not agree with the time measured from a point on the surface of the Earth. Let us consider two special kinds of orbits, Polar and Equatorial, as pictured in Figure 5-4. Orbits which are neither Polar nor Equatorial are called *intermediate*. The Earth, of course, rotates under a satellite as it orbits. A satellite in a Polar orbit would cross a given parallel of latitude during each orbit at a distance west of its previous crossing. There would be no differences in measurement of the period, however, since time intervals remain constant within a time zone. A satellite moving east, however, in an Equatorial orbit will after one complete circle be behind the observer on Earth, who will have moved east because of the rotation of the

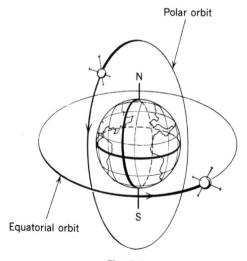

Fig. 5-4

Earth. By the time the satellite is again over the observer, it will have traveled through a little more than one orbit, and the observer's measurement, if not corrected, will indicate a period greater than the true period. For intermediate orbits, the error will depend on the direction of the orbit and the angle it makes with the Equator.

The Mercury spacecraft were orbited at altitudes of about 100 miles. At this altitude the atmosphere is so thin that it offers almost no resistance to the motion of the spacecraft, and a relatively stable orbit can be achieved. The velocity needed to place an object in orbit at this altitude can be readily calculated from equation (35). The radius of the orbit will be 3960 + 100 or 4060 miles. The velocity required is

$$v = \sqrt{\frac{9.56 \, (10^4)}{4060}} = \sqrt{23.5}$$ or 4.85 miles per second, which is

equal approximately to 17,500 miles per hour. Since the circumference of the orbit is 2(3.14)(4060) or about 25,000 miles, the time required for one orbit will be $\frac{25,000}{17,000} = 1.43$

hours or about 86 minutes.

Let us compute the velocity and period for a circular orbit at the surface of the Moon. Since the Moon has a mass equal to .012 times the mass of the Earth, we multiply the value of M in equation (34), representing the mass of the Earth, by .012. The radius of the Moon is found from the table on page

47 to be 1080 miles. We thus have $v = \sqrt{\frac{9.56 \, (.012)(10^4)}{1080}}$

$= \sqrt{1.06} = 1.03$ miles per second, or 3700 miles per hour. The

period of the orbit will be $\frac{2(3.14)(1080)}{3700} = \frac{6783}{3700} = 1.83$ hours

or 110 minutes. Note that, in spite of its smaller radius, a surface orbit has a lower velocity on the Moon than on the Earth because of the Moon's much weaker gravity.

Space Flights

5-5. Echo I, a spherical balloon 100 feet in diameter made of aluminum coated polyester film, was put into orbit about

1000 miles above the Earth on August 12, 1960. It was used as an experimental communications satellite to reflect radio waves to an area distant from their origin. Because of its size, Echo I was easily visible at night to the naked eye, and it looked like a bright star moving across the sky. Compute the velocity and period of Echo I.

5-6. Suppose, in the following drawing, that an observer standing at night at point B with an unobstructed view of the horizon is searching for Echo I. Use trigonometric functions to find the number of degrees in angle BOC. Knowing the period of the orbit, compute the length of time that Echo I would be visible to the observer, from the time when it appeared on the horizon at A until it disappeared below the horizon at C.

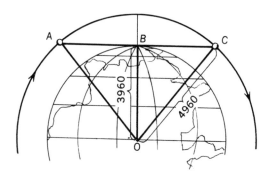

5-7. A satellite at an altitude of 100 miles is moving east in an Equatorial orbit. Its true period is about 86 minutes, or 1.43 hours. During each hour the observer on Earth moves east 1/24 of a rotation, and the satellite must travel an extra distance to "catch" the observer. What will be the period of the orbit as measured by the observer's clock?

5-8. Suppose the above satellite is moving west. What will be the period of the orbit as measured by the observer's clock?

5-9. Compute the velocity and period for an orbit 60 miles above the surface of the Moon.

5-10. What effect does the mass of a satellite have upon its orbital velocity?

5-11. An alternate formula for finding the velocity required to achieve an orbit is

$$v = \sqrt{\frac{g\ R^2}{r}}, \tag{36}$$

in which R is the radius of the Earth, g is the acceleration of gravity at the surface of the Earth, and r is the radius of the orbit. This formula will obviously give the same results yielded by formula (35) provided $GM - gR^2$. Verify by computation that these quantities are equal. (Remember that the units of measure involved are miles and seconds, and therefore the value of g must be expressed in miles per second per second.)

5-12. Use equation (35) to find the velocity and period of the Earth in its orbit about the Sun. Note from the table on page 47 that the mass of the Sun is 330,000 times the mass of the Earth. Evidently $r = 93,000,000$ miles.

The Synchronous Orbit

It is obvious that as the altitude of an orbit about a given body increases, the period also increases. A project of much interest has been to place a satellite in an orbit for which the period is 24 hours. Such a "synchronous" satellite, if placed in a west-to-east orbit over the Equator, would revolve in its orbit at the same rate at which the Earth rotates on its axis, and to an observer on Earth it would appear to "stand still" in space or appear to be stationary over the Earth. The first Syncom, placed in orbit by NASA during the summer of 1963, is in a nearly synchronous orbit. Remaining constantly over the Atlantic Ocean between South America and Africa, it can be used to beam communication signals to over one billion people in North and South America, Western Europe, and Africa.

Calculate the velocity and altitude required to place a satellite in a synchronous orbit. The distance traveled by the satellite during one revolution will be $2\pi r$, where r is the radius of the orbit. Let t be the time in seconds required for one revolution. Since there is to be one revolution per day, $t = 24(3600)$ seconds. The velocity is distance divided by the time, or

$$v = \frac{2\pi r}{t}.$$

But
$$v = \sqrt{\frac{9.56\,(10^4)}{r}}.$$

Therefore
$$\frac{2\pi r}{t} = \sqrt{\frac{9.56\,(10^4)}{r}}$$

$$\left(\frac{2\pi r}{t}\right)^2 r = 9.56\,(10^4)$$

$$r^3 = \frac{9.56\,(10^4)\,(24)^2\,(3600)^2}{4\,(3.14)^2} = 18{,}100 \times 10^9$$

$$r = \sqrt[3]{18{,}100} \times 10^3 = 26{,}260.$$

The altitude above the Earth then equals $26{,}260 - 3{,}960$ or $22{,}300$ miles.

$$v = \sqrt{\frac{9.56\,(10^4)}{26{,}260}} = \sqrt{3.64} = 1.91 \text{ miles per second}$$

or 6880 miles per hour.

Syncom I was put into orbit with a complicated flight plan. It was rocketed by a Delta launch vehicle from Cape Kennedy into a long elliptical orbit beginning with a velocity of 33,550 feet per second, or 18,300 miles per hour. This enormous speed enabled it to coast upward, gradually slowing as it climbed. About 5¼ hours after launch it reached apogee, its greatest distance from Earth, which was 22,300 miles. Its velocity was then down to 4800 feet per second. If not further accelerated at this point, it would curve back to Earth, following an elliptical orbit.

But at this point a spaceman's technique called a "kick in the apogee" was used. A small solid-fuel rocket motor on board was fired to kick Syncom from its initial elliptical path into a circular orbit. The motor, ignited by a timing device aboard the satellite or by ground command, gave the satellite the additional "horizontal" velocity required to push it into a circular orbit.

Space Flights

5-13. The table below gives the data we have computed for orbits at several different altitudes above the Earth. Enter on the fourth line the velocity and period you found for Echo I. Fill in the other empty blanks.

Altitude (In miles above the Earth)	Velocity (Miles per hour)	Period
0	17,600	85 minutes
100	17,500	86 minutes
500	?	?
1,000	?	?
22,300	6,880	24 hours
?	?	48 hours
234,000	?	?

The altitude on the last line refers, of course, to the distance to the Moon. Although the table for the sake of consistency gives the distance of the Moon's center above the surface of the Earth, computations should be based upon 239,000 miles,

the distance between the centers of the Earth and Moon. The observed period of the Moon is approximately 27⅓ days.

5-14. Three Syncoms evenly spaced on a circle around the Earth could form a world-wide communications network covering the entire Earth. If this were true, it would be necessary that each Syncom be able to "see" at least one-third of the surface of the Earth. If Syncom is at point S in the drawing on the previous page, the area that can be "seen" is a zone with altitude $CD = h$. Remember that the area S of a zone is given by the formula $S = 2\pi rh$. Evidently the length of SC is 22,300 miles, and $CE = r = 3,960$ miles. Find what percent of the Earth's surface lies within the zone.

Orbital Paths

Our discussion about orbits has been based upon the assumption that orbits are circular. We can be quite sure, however, that the orbit of any body moving under the influence of gravity is not a perfect circle. The circle will always be flattened a little so that the orbit becomes an ellipse. In actual practice an orbit will not even be a perfect ellipse. The Earth is neither a perfect sphere nor of uniform density, so the pull of gravity varies somewhat from place to place. Furthermore, there are gravity pulls from the Moon, the Sun, and the planets. Any orbit will have perturbations, or deviations from the theoretical path.

It can be shown that every theoretical orbit is a conic section. Conic sections are discussed in detail in textbooks on analytical geometry. If a complete cone (of two nappes and infinite extent), as illustrated in Figure 5-5, is cut by a plane, the cross section formed is a conic section. If the cutting plane is perpendicular to the axis PQ, the section formed is a circle, illustrated at A. If the plane is inclined at an angle, but still cuts entirely across the cone, the section is an ellipse, as at B. If the plane is parallel to a rectilinear element of the cone, as XY, the section is a parabola, illustrated at C. If the plane cuts both nappes of the cone, the section is a hyperbola, as at D and D'. It is obvious that the path of a body in a closed

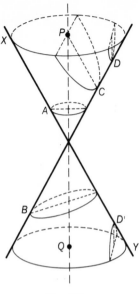

Fig. 5-5

orbit is a circle or ellipse. Parabolas and hyperbolas give open or "escape" orbits.

Another way of defining the ellipse is to say it is the path of a point which moves so that the sum of its distances from two fixed points is a constant. In Figure 5-6 the two fixed points are F and F'. They are called the foci of the ellipse. The sum of the distances of P, and of every point on the ellipse, from F and F' is $2a$. Each focus is located a distance c from O, the center of the ellipse. The ratio $\dfrac{c}{a}$ is called the eccentricity e of the ellipse, and is a measure of the "roundness" of the ellipse. We can see from the drawing that when $c = 0$, making the eccentricity zero, the points F and F' will coincide with the center O and the ellipse becomes a circle, an ellipse with zero eccentricity.

It is apparent from Figure 5-6 that the length of the major axis of the ellipse is $2a$, while the length of the minor axis is $2b$. Thus a and b are respectively called the semi-major axis

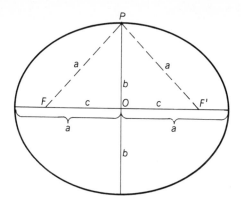

Fig. 5-6

and the semi-minor axis of the ellipse. It is also evident, by use of the Pythagorean Theorem, that $b^2 + c^2 = a^2$. Eccentricity can therefore be defined as

$$e = \frac{c}{a} = \frac{\sqrt{a^2 - b^2}}{a}. \qquad (37)$$

When $a = b$, $e = 0$, and the ellipse becomes a circle. When the eccentricity is large, $a > b$, and the ellipse becomes flattened and stretched out.

The mathematical expressions that relate the apogee and perigee distances to the shape of an elliptical orbit are rather simple. In Figure 5-7, suppose that a satellite S is in an elliptical orbit around the Earth, which is located at one focus of the ellipse. If the apogee and perigee distances are measured from the center of the Earth, it is readily apparent that:

$$a = \tfrac{1}{2}(A + P) \qquad (38)$$
$$c = a - P = \tfrac{1}{2}(A + P) - P$$

or $\qquad c = \tfrac{1}{2}(A - P) \qquad (39)$

$$e = \frac{c}{a} = \frac{\tfrac{1}{2}(A - P)}{\tfrac{1}{2}(A + P)}$$

or $\qquad e = \frac{A - P}{A + P} \qquad (40)$

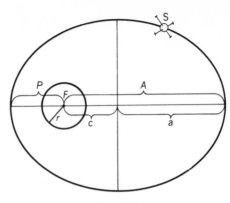

Fig. 5-7

Thus if we know the apogee (highest point) and perigee (lowest point) of an orbit, we can describe accurately the ellipse. Sputnik I, orbited by the Russians in October 1957, had an apogee and perigee of 583 miles and 132 miles respectively above the surface of the Earth, or 4543 and 4092 miles from the center of the Earth. The eccentricity was $\frac{4543 - 4092}{4543 + 4092} = \frac{451}{8653} = .052$. Since the eccentricity was very small, we know that the orbit was nearly circular. Therefore the value of b, the semi-minor axis of the ellipse, should be nearly as large as a. By equations (38) and (39), $a = \frac{1}{2}(4543 + 4092) = 4318$, while $c = \frac{1}{2}(4543 - 4092) = 226$. By the Pythagorean equation, $b = \sqrt{4318^2 - 226^2} = \sqrt{18,594,048} = 4312$ miles.

It is interesting to note that the velocity of an object in an elliptical orbit is not constant. John Kepler early in the 17th Century studied the motions of the planets and stated three conclusions, known as Kepler's Laws. His Second Law relates the velocity of a satellite to its position in orbit, as follows: "Each planet revolves in such a way that the line joining it to the Sun sweeps over equal areas in equal intervals of time." Suppose that the three areas swept out by the radial line in Figure 5-8 are equal. (The satellite is revolving around the

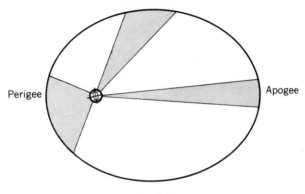

Fig. 5-8

Earth rather than the Sun, but the law still holds.) It is clear that when the radial line is long, the corresponding arc of the ellipse must be short; and when the radial distance is short, the related arc traversed must be longer in order for the areas to be equal. But the satellite traverses these shorter and longer arcs in equal intervals of time. The satellite will be traveling at its lowest velocity when it is at apogee. When it leaves apogee and sweeps back toward the Earth, its speed will gradually increase, until it is traveling with its greatest velocity when it reaches perigee.

Finding the velocity of a satellite at any given point in an elliptical orbit is beyond the scope of the mathematics in this book. However the velocities at the special points, apogee and perigee, can be found with rather simple equations. If v_A and v_P are the velocities at these two points respectively, A and P are the apogee and perigee distances respectively when measured from the center of the Earth, and e is the eccentricity of the orbit, the two equations are:

$$v_A = \sqrt{\frac{GM}{A}(1-e)} \qquad (41)$$

$$v_P = \sqrt{\frac{GM}{P}(1+e)}. \qquad (42)$$

By direct reasoning from Kepler's Second Law, or by dividing equation (41) by equation (42), we obtain the following very simple relationship between the two velocities:

$$\frac{v_A}{v_P} = \frac{P}{A} \tag{43}$$

Let us apply the above equations to the data for Sputnik I.

$$v_A = \sqrt{\frac{9.56(10^4)}{4543}(1 - .052)} = \sqrt{\frac{90.608}{4543}}$$

$$= \sqrt{20} = 4.72 \text{ miles per second or } 16{,}700 \text{ miles per hour.}$$

By equation (43), $v_P = \dfrac{(A)v_A}{P} = \dfrac{4543 \times 16{,}700}{4092} = 18{,}800$ miles

per hour. Since the orbit of Sputnik I was very nearly circular, there was not a large difference between the velocities at apogee and perigee. However if a satellite is in a highly eccentric elliptical orbit with a perigee of 100 to 150 miles, the high speeds of the satellite at perigee result in a significant amount of heating from friction with the very thin atmosphere at that altitude. The result is a loss of energy, so that the satellite does not reach quite as high a point at the next apogee. When the apogee point becomes lower and lower, the orbit of the satellite tends to become more and more circular.

Period of an Elliptical Orbit

Previously in this chapter we found the period, p_c, of a circular orbit by simply dividing the circumference of the orbit by the velocity of the satellite. If we had formally derived a formula for the period, we should have obtained the following formula:

$$p_c = 2\pi \sqrt{\frac{r^3}{GM}}. \tag{44}$$

Another way of stating equation (18), Kepler's Third Law, is that the ratio of the square of the period of the satellite to the cube of the mean radius of its orbit is a constant. If we let the mean radius $\frac{1}{2}(A + P) = a$, it can be shown that the period p_e of an elliptical orbit about the Earth is given by

$$p_e = 2\pi \sqrt{\frac{a^3}{GM}}. \qquad (45)$$

Comparison of these two equations shows that the period in an elliptical orbit is the same as for a circular orbit with radius equal to the mean radius of the elliptical orbit.

It is interesting to compare the behavior of satellites in orbits so related that the apogee of an elliptical orbit is just equal to the radius of a circular orbit. Two such orbits are pictured in Figure 5-9. Intuitively it would appear that the period in the elliptical orbit must be much less than in the circular orbit because the path is so much shorter. But intuition is not always a sure guide. First let us compare the velocities at apogee in the two orbits. Comparing equations (34) and (41), we note

that $v_A < v$ if $\dfrac{GM}{A}(1 - e) < \dfrac{GM}{r}$. Since $A = r$, $\dfrac{GM}{A} = \dfrac{GM}{r}$. The

controlling factor then is $(1 - e)$. Since for an elliptical orbit $0 < e < 1$, $0 < (1 - e) < 1$. Thus the presence of $(1 - e)$ always reduces the value under the radical sign, and v_A is

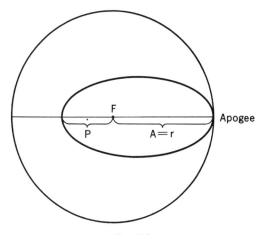

Fig. 5-9

always less than v. Note also that as $e \to 1$, $(1 - e) \to 0$, and v_A may become very small. Thus the low velocity at apogee in an elliptical orbit may considerably increase the period.

Let us therefore compare the periods directly. The two periods, expressed in terms of the labels in the drawing, are:

$$p_c = 2\pi \sqrt{\frac{r^3}{GM}}$$

and

$$p_e = 2\pi \sqrt{\frac{\left(\frac{r + P}{2}\right)^3}{GM}}.$$

Obviously $p_c > p_e$ if $r^3 > \left(\dfrac{r + P}{2}\right)^3$. This relationship can be investigated with the following series of inequalities:

$$r > P$$
$$r + r = 2r > r + P$$
$$r > \frac{r + P}{2}$$
$$r^3 > \left(\frac{r + P}{2}\right)^3.$$

Space technicians use the technique mentioned previously in the discussion of Syncom for changing an elliptical orbit into a circular one. When the satellite is traveling, with its lowest velocity, through apogee, a small rocket engine is fired to give an increase in speed. This "kick in the apogee" accelerates the satellite to a higher velocity and delays the descent to perigee, making the orbit more circular.

Let us suppose that a satellite weighing 800 pounds is orbiting the Earth with an apogee of 1000 miles and a perigee of 150 miles. Then $A = 4960$, $P = 4110$, and $e = \dfrac{4960 - 4110}{4960 + 4110} = \dfrac{850}{9070} = .0947$. Thus $v_A = \sqrt{\dfrac{9.56(10^4)}{4960}(1 - .0947)} = \sqrt{18.3}$ $= 4.27$ miles per second or 15,400 miles per hour. We found in *space flight* 5-13 that the velocity in a circular orbit 1000 miles above the surface of the Earth is 15,700 miles per hour. An apogee motor with a 50-pound thrust is on board the satellite, and we wish to give it a command to fire for a time long enough to push the satellite into a circular orbit. The gain in speed needed is $15,700 - 15,400 = 300$ miles per hour or about 440 feet per second. By equation (9), the acceleration produced by the motor is $a = \dfrac{50 \times 32.2}{800} = 2.01$ feet per second per second. By equation (3) the firing time needed is $t = \dfrac{440}{2.01} = 219$ seconds.

Space Flights

5-15. Explorer I, orbited by the United States in February 1958, had an apogee and perigee of approximately 1580 miles and 220 miles respectively. Find the eccentricity of the orbit. Find the semi-major and semi-minor axes.

5-16. Lunik 3, orbited by the Russians in October 1958, had a highly elliptical orbit, with apogee of about 292,000 miles and perigee of about 25,300 miles. Find the eccentricity of the orbit. Find the velocities at apogee and perigee.

5-17. Echo I, orbited by the United States in August 1960, had an apogee and perigee of approximately 1050 and 950 miles respectively. Find the eccentricity of the orbit.

5-18. The orbit of a satellite around the Earth has a semi-major axis of 10,000 miles and a semi-minor axis of 9,000 miles. Find its apogee, perigee, and the eccentricity of the ellipse.

5-19. Explorer 18 was sent into orbit by NASA from Cape Kennedy on November 26, 1963. Its orbit was a rather "flat" ellipse, with a perigee of 119 miles and an apogee of 122,000 miles. Find its eccentricity. Find the velocity at perigee and apogee. What additional velocity would have been needed at apogee to push Explorer into a circular orbit?

5-20. *Friendship 7*, in which John H. Glenn, Jr. made the first manned orbital space flight for the United States, had a perigee of 100 miles and an eccentricity of .0076. Find its apogee.

5-21. We found that the velocity of Syncom in a circular

orbit is 6880 miles per hour. NASA reported that when Syncom I reached apogee, it had a velocity of 4800 feet per second. What additional velocity, in feet per second, did the apogee motor need to push Syncom into a circular orbit?

5-22. Since we know v_A and A for Syncom I, we can readily solve equation (41), for e. Knowing e, we can use equation (40) to find P, and then equation (42) to find v_P. Solve these equations and find out what orbit Syncom would be following if the apogee motor had failed to fire.

5-23. Combine equations (41) and (42) to obtain equation (43).

5-24. What meaning could you give to the quantities v_A and A in equation (41) if $e = 1$?

5-25. What relationship must exist between apogee and perigee distances if the velocity at perigee is to be exactly two times the velocity at apogee? n times the velocity at apogee? Does the eccentricity increase or decrease as the value of n increases?

Escape Velocity

In the previous discussions we have been concerned with orbits that are elliptical, so that the satellite continues to revolve about the Earth or another body. However, not all orbits are elliptical. Some comets, for example, follow orbits which are hyperbolic. If a spacecraft visits the Moon, or other parts of the Solar System, it must overcome the gravitational pull of the Earth and may need to follow an orbit which is not elliptical. As noted previously, all orbits controlled by natural gravitational forces follow one of the conic sections. The conic sections are differentiated from each other by their eccentricity. Analytical geometry proves that conic sections may be classified in terms of the eccentricity e as follows:

A circle if $e = 0$
An ellipse if $0 < e < 1$
A parabola if $e = 1$
A hyperbola if $e > 1$.

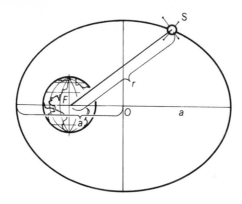

Fig. 5-10

Let Figure 5-10 represent a satellite which is in an orbit related to the Earth. The center of the Earth is at F, a focus of the conic section. The "radial" distance to the satellite is r, and a is the semi-major axis of an ellipse. A more general form of the formula which expresses the relationship between the velocity and radius of an orbit is

$$v = \sqrt{GM\left(\frac{2}{r} - \frac{1}{a}\right)},\qquad(46)$$

in which r and a are the quantities in Figure 5-10. When the focus F is at the center O of the conic, $r = a$, the orbit is a circle, the eccentricity is zero, and the formula reduces to equation (34). When the eccentricity is one, the ellipse opens out to become a parabola, and the second focus is at infinity. The value of a becomes infinitely large so that the ratio $\frac{1}{a} \to 0$, and the equation reduces to

$$v = \sqrt{\frac{2\ GM}{r}}.\qquad(47)$$

Equation (41) may be rewritten as $v = \sqrt{2}\sqrt{\frac{GM}{r}}$. The velocity needed to achieve a parabolic or escape orbit is obtained by simply multiplying the circular orbit velocity by $\sqrt{2}$, or by approximately 1.41. If the velocity imparted to a satellite is greater than the parabolic, or minimum, escape velocity, the satellite simply follows a hyperbolic orbit, and the eccentricity is greater than one.

The various possibilities for achieving an orbit are illustrated in Figure 5-11. Suppose an object is thrust from the Earth at point P. Failing to go into an orbit, it will fall back to Earth at some point N. If it achieves a circular orbit, it will follow the circle c. If the orbit is elliptical, it will follow a path similar to e. If the velocity is just equal to escape velocity, it will follow the parabolic path p. If the velocity is greater than the minimum needed for escape, it will follow a hyperbolic path, as at h. Most escape orbits will be hyperbolas; the velocity probably will never exactly equal $\sqrt{2}$ times circular velocity.

We found that the velocity needed to achieve a circular orbit at the surface of the Earth is 17,600 miles per hour. The escape velocity at the Earth's surface is $17,600 \times 1.41 = 24,800$ miles per hour. This number is usually rounded to 25,000 miles per hour. The escape velocity at an altitude 100 miles

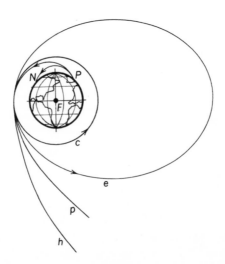

Fig. 5-11

above the Earth is found from our previous work to be 17,500 × 1.41 or 24,700 miles per hour.

Escape velocity is intimately related to factors controlling the environment on a planet. When the escape velocity is low, it is easy for the molecules of the gases composing an atmosphere to escape into space. With no protecting atmosphere, no surface water can collect, there is no protection from cosmic rays, and no protecting blanket to moderate surface temperatures. Because of their low escape velocities it is highly unlikely there is any atmosphere on the Moon or Mercury. The planets with higher escape velocities do have atmospheres, but it is not known whether they will support life as we know it or permit man to live on them. Mars has a higher escape velocity than either the Moon or Mercury and is able to hold a thin atmosphere, about equal in density to the Earth's atmosphere at an altitude of 56,000 feet. Jupiter has such a high escape velocity that it is able to hold a very dense atmosphere. It is estimated that the atmosphere of Jupiter is 1000 miles deep, and the atmospheric pressure at the surface is so great it probably would crush an Earth man.

We have referred to escape velocity as the velocity needed to permit escape from the gravitational attraction of the Earth or other body. This concept needs clarification for two reasons. (1) Although a body can escape from the vicinity of the Earth, it can never escape from the Earth's gravitational field, since the gravitational attraction of any body extends infinitely far. Escape velocity is simply that velocity which enables a body escaping from Earth to travel at lower and lower speeds as the pull of gravity slows it down and still have enough energy left to keep on going. (2) An escape from Earth does not necessarily require an escape orbit. If a spacecraft motor could supply a long-lasting thrust sufficiently strong to overcome the attraction of gravity and have a few pounds left over for propulsion, the craft could move directly away from the Earth with a very small acceleration, but reaching a high velocity after a period of several days. If sources of continuous long-lasting power could be developed, spacecraft could be steered and maneuvered through space at will.

Space Flights

5-26. Calculate the escape velocity for all of the other altitudes listed in the table in *space flight* 5-13.

5-27. Compute the orbital velocity, period, and escape velocity for an altitude 100 miles above the surface of Mars.

5-28. Compute the orbital velocity, period, and escape velocity for an altitude 50 miles above the surface of Venus.

5-29. An elliptical orbit around the Moon has an apogee of 100 miles and a perigee of 50 miles. Find the eccentricity.

5-30. Verify that the figures given for surface escape velocity on page 47 are correct for Mars, Mercury, Moon, and Saturn.

6

Flights in Space

Difference Between Atmospheric and Space Flight

A craft which travels through the atmosphere is designed to take advantage of the air for lift, motion, and guidance. In heavier-than-air craft such as airplanes, the wings are designed so that when the craft is in motion, the pressure over the wing is less than the pressure under the wing. The difference in pressure provides lift. Motion is produced by a propeller, which cuts into the air like a screw, or by thrust from a jet engine. Oxygen from the air is used for combustion. Vanes or fins use the resistance of the air to provide guidance. Lighter-than-air craft, like balloons or dirigibles, float in air as ships float on water.

Spacecraft, on the other hand, are handicapped by the air. They are much more efficient above the atmosphere. Although air resistance is necessary to slow down a spacecraft when it re-enters the atmosphere, during other phases of its flight the air is an obstacle. The drag caused by the air on take-off results in a considerable waste of power. Lift and guidance are accomplished by the thrust or push supplied by rocket engines. Rocket engines differ from jet engines in that a rocket carries its own supply of oxygen for combustion, and the rocket motor can operate in the vacuum above the atmosphere.

There are two general methods by which a spacecraft travels in space. One is to "blast off" with a high acceleration producing enough velocity to place the spacecraft into a gravitational orbit. Once in orbit, the rest of the ride is "free." The spacecraft is said to be in "free fall," and it behaves as dictated by the laws of gravity. The craft acts like a missile and follows a ballistic trajectory. The alternate method of traveling in space is the low-power long-time method. As noted in the previous chapter, if a booster had just enough thrust to overcome the force of gravity, it could rise steadily from the ground. Even though the acceleration is small, it could develop tremendous speed over a long enough period of time. This method, requiring a steady long-lasting supply of power, is not considered practical with present equipment and fuels. However, as we shall see in a later section, travel during the next few years to points in the Solar System may well be done by a combination of both methods.

Atmospheric Resistance

When a body is moving through the atmosphere, there is always some resistance offered by the air. This resistance tends to slow the vehicle and, at high speeds, to heat it considerably. A simple formula by Newton expressing this resistance is

$$R = \rho A v^2, \tag{48}$$

where R is the resistance, ρ is the air density, A is the effective area of the cross section of the moving object, and v is the velocity of the object. Although we cannot give numerical values to these quantities without knowing specific data about a given situation, we can study this equation to see its implications. We know ρ, the air density, varies with altitude, and the density is approximately halved for each 3¼ miles increase in altitude. Let us assume A, the area of the cross section of the object, is constant. During a launch the resistance related to the density of the air will gradually diminish as the launch vehicle gains altitude. However, since the air drag on the vehicle increases as the square of the velocity, the rapidly increasing speed may offset the decrease in resistance resulting from the decreasing density. It is obvious that during launch it is highly desirable that the vehicle be designed so the area A of the effective cross section is small.

The problem of re-entry is best studied by solving the equation for v, so that

$$v = \sqrt{\frac{R}{\rho A}}.$$

We want v, the velocity, to be small when the descending craft reaches the surface of the Earth. The quantity v will be small if ρ and A are large. The air resistance ρ doubles for each 3¼ miles of vertical descent. The cross section A can be made large by providing some kind of wing or one or more parachutes. A properly designed spacecraft can take advantage of characteristics of the atmosphere for safe landing.

Space Flights

6-1. What will be the resistance R at high altitudes where for all practical purposes $\rho = 0$?

6-2. Assuming that ρ is directly proportional to the density of the atmosphere and that R and A remain constant, what decrease in velocity would take place during a descent of 13 miles through the atmosphere?

Weightless

A body in orbit is said to be in a condition of "weightlessness." Weightlessness, often called "zero gravity" or "free fall," does not mean a change in the condition of the spacecraft or the absence of gravity. It means that the attraction of gravity has been balanced by the centrifugal force so that the spacecraft and objects within it act as if the force of gravity, which gives weight to objects, no longer existed. In a condition of weightlessness, many processes that we take for granted on Earth cannot occur. Normal movements, such as walking, would cause the astronaut to push himself away from the "floor" and perhaps crash violently against the "ceiling." In fact, there would be no "down" or "up." To move about on a spaceship requires hand rails or magnetized shoes. Liquids would not pour from a vessel, but would form into globules floating in mid-air. Eating with a spoon or drinking from a cup would be impossible, since food without weight would not stay in them. Liquids would be dispensed from squeeze bottles. The biological and psychological effects of weightlessness will require much study.

However, even though objects are weightless, they still possess mass and inertia. Objects floating within a spacecraft could collide with other objects and break them. A workman in his spacesuit assembling a space station could be crushed between two massive though weightless sections that were drifting together. The worker would, unless tethered to the space platform or equipped with jets for propulsion, float away in space forever if he pushed himself away from the platform.

Space Flights

6-3. A camera weighing one pound is accidentally given a three-pound push for one-tenth second by an astronaut. With what velocity will it strike the wall of the spacecraft four feet away?

6-4. Two sections of a space platform each weighing one ton are moving together with a relative velocity of one inch

Fig. 6-1.   Man in space needs the safeguard of a tether. (NASA)

per second. They meet and come to rest 0.01 seconds. With what force will they come together? (Use the equation for impulse, $Ft = \dfrac{W}{g} v$, in which the same quantities and units are used as in other equations of motion found in Chapter 1.)

6-5. A worker helping assemble a space station accidentally lets a wrench slip from his hand. With what acceleration will it fall?

6-6. A mechanic, who dressed in his spacesuit would weigh 170 pounds on Earth, pushes himself away from a space station which he is helping to assemble with a force of 10 pounds lasting for one second. With what velocity will he move away in space from the station?

Artificial Gravity

To avoid the problem of weightlessness, it has been suggested that artificial gravity be created in spacecraft and space stations or terminals. Many designs have been suggested for the construction of space stations. One of the early designs suggested for a space station calls for it to be built as a hollow circular tube like a bicycle tire. The station would then be given a rotary motion about its central axis. This motion would create a centrifugal force which would be completely indistinguishable from gravity. Regardless of the orientation or attitude of the station, the center of the wheel would be "up" and the rim would be "down." People could stroll in comfort about the station while waiting for the next space flight to Mars, Earth, or other destinations. Everything would stay in place in the station.

If the number of revolutions of the station per second is N, then we have the formula

$$N = \frac{1}{2\pi} \sqrt{\frac{a}{r}}, \tag{49}$$

where a is the desired acceleration of artificial gravity and r is the distance in feet from a point in the station to the center of rotation. With this equation we can tailor the amount of

Fig. 6-2. Artist's concept of a space station. (NASA)

gravity provided to suit our needs or preferences. Suppose that our space station has a radius of 250 feet, and we wish to create at the rim of the station an artificial gravity equal to the surface gravity of the Earth. Then $a = 32.2$, and

$$N = \frac{1}{2(3.14)} \sqrt{\frac{32.2}{250}} = \frac{.358}{6.28} = .057.$$

The spaceship should rotate at the rate of 0.057 rotations per second or 3.42 rotations per minute.

Space Flights

6-7. Suppose that the "ceiling" or inner rim of the wheel in the above station is 30 feet from the "floor" or outer rim. Then the radius at the ceiling is 220 feet. What is the force of the artificial gravity created at the ceiling?

6-8. How many rotations per minute would be needed to create gravity equal to half the surface gravity on the Earth at the outer rim of the above station?

6-9. A larger station has an outside diameter of 1000 feet. It has two levels, the outside diameter of the inner level being 960 feet. What number of rotations per minute would be needed to create Earth surface gravity at the floor of the outer level? What would be the gravitational force at the floor of the inner level?

6-10. How many rotations per minute would create a gravity of 20 feet per second per second at the floor of the outer level of the above station?

Changing Orbits

A spacecraft with a long-lasting source of power and sufficient thrust to overcome gravity could be steered through space in much the same way an automobile is steered on land or an airplane is steered through the air. The craft would be equipped with jets, or sources of thrust, located in various positions around its exterior. By adjusting the force and direction of the jets, we could accelerate or retard the craft or move it up, down, or to the side with less reference to orbits or gravitational forces. However, long-lasting sources of power with sufficient thrust have not yet been developed. Those power sources which last for relatively long periods of time give a very low thrust. Space flights in the immediate future must follow as much as possible natural orbits, taking advantage of the forces of gravity.

Suppose a space flight begins with placement of the craft into a circular orbit. The craft carries a source of propulsion of relatively low power. It is possible to direct the propulsion particles so that the craft is either speeded up or slowed down. If the speed of the spacecraft is increased, it is pushed into a higher orbit. If the increased speed lasts only for a while, the effect is to raise the point of apogee and thereby change the orbit from circular to elliptical. If the thrust from the space-craft motor is strong enough and lasts long enough, the velocity of the craft may be increased to escape velocity, and the orbit will become parabolic or hyperbolic. However, if the thrust is applied so that it reduces the speed of the spacecraft, the craft will move into a lower orbit, and if the reduction in speed is great enough, the craft will begin to spiral down for a landing on the body about which it is orbiting.

Consider a spacecraft, whose surface weight is three tons, in orbit around the Earth with a velocity of 17,500 miles per hour, or about 25,700 feet per second. It has an engine producing a thrust of only 10 pounds. What will be the velocity of the craft after 100 hours? By equation (9), the acceleration produced by the engine is $a = \dfrac{f \, g}{w} = \dfrac{10 \times 32.2}{6000} = .054$ feet per second. The velocity produced in 100 hours is $v = at = .054 \times 100 \times 3600 = 19,440$ feet per second or about 13,300 miles per hour. The total speed of the craft will be $17,500 + 13,300$ or 30,800 miles per hour. Long before 100 hours has elapsed the craft will have moved into a hyperbolic escape orbit.

A number of facts about the mechanics of the Solar System are very favorable for interplanetary travel by spacecraft. The planes of the orbits of the planets are nearly coincidental. This fact simplifies interplanetary guidance problems and lowers the energy requirements for movement among the planets. All of the planets move about the Sun in the same direction. Thus the orbital speed of the planet from which the spaceship departs gives it an initial velocity in a launch to another planet. In addition, the planets rotate about their axes in the same direction in which they revolve about the Sun, so that the spacecraft gets an additional push by taking off in the direction of rotation. The fact that all of the planetary orbits are nearly circular means that energy requirements for changing from one planetary orbit to another are almost the same for all points of departure along an orbit.

Space Flights

6-11. A craft weighing 175 tons have been envisioned for making a trip to Mars and back. It has an ion propulsion engine which provides 60 pounds of thrust. If it begins its trip from a circular orbit 1000 miles above the surface of the Earth, what will be its velocity after one month? What distance will it have traveled in space during that time?

6-12. An experimental solar engine has been described which uses mirrors to gather from the Sun heat which is used to expand hydrogen gas. The heated gas will emerge as a jet giving a thrust of about 2 pounds. If the solar engine begins to work after the craft, weighing 40 tons, has been placed in a parabolic escape orbit beginning 500 miles above the surface of the Earth, what is the total velocity attained and distance covered after 80 hours? After 80 days?

6-13. A Solar sail has been described which will produce an acceleration of 0.01 g. What increase in velocity would it give to a 25-ton craft in 30 days?

6-14. A 3000-pound spacecraft is in orbit with a velocity of 17,400 miles per hour. For what length of time must a reverse thrust of 500 pounds operate to slow its speed down to 17,100 miles per hour?

Rendezvous and Docking

The dictionary defines the word rendezvous to mean a meeting or an arrangement for a meeting between two or more persons. Thus the meeting of two spacecraft in space is called *rendezvous*. The mechanical joining or linking of the craft is called docking. The two craft will undoubtedly be built so that they can be joined automatically upon contact. One possibility is to arrange that a recess in one will just accept and hold securely a projection on the other. It will be necessary for the two craft to have orbital speeds such that the second craft slowly overtakes the first one. Learning how to maneuver the two craft so that they meet and join in space represents one of the technical problems on which space scientists are now working.

Obviously two craft in the same orbit cannot rendezvous, since they would both be moving at the same speed and the one could not overtake the other. If a craft is moved to a

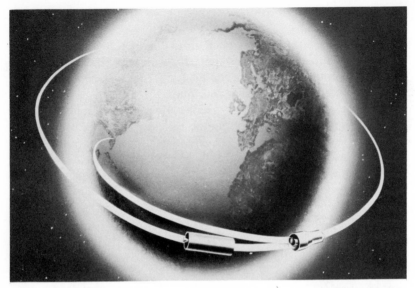

Fig. 6-3. Rendezvous requires the merging of two orbits. (NASA)

lower orbit, its orbital speed will increase and it can overtake the leading craft, but they will be at different altitudes and therefore will not come together. It appears that a modification, as needed, of orbital paths will be required. Low-thrust engines located in various positions about the spacecraft can be used to increase or decrease velocities and modify orbits so that one craft overtakes the other at the point where their individual orbital paths intersect. Eventually large space stations or terminals may be permanently located several thousand miles above the Earth. Rendezvous and docking with the space station will be required whenever a craft from Earth or a planet arrives with supplies or passengers. The required techniques of rendezvous undoubtedly will be changed and improved as our knowledge of space science and space technology grows and as long-lasting sources of adequate thrust are developed.

Tracking of Spacecraft

Several types of systems are used for tracking objects in space. One method is optical tracking with telescopic cameras.

Another system utilizes large dish-shaped receiving antennas for receiving radio signals. This type of system, combined with powerful transmitters, not only keeps track of the location of a spacecraft but assures almost constant contact with astronauts on manned spacecraft. Small unmanned satellites are efficiently tracked with the STADAN system, Space Tracking and Data Acquisition Network. This system requires that the satellite carry a tiny transmitter. Since the transmitter is small, the system was formerly called Minimum Weight Tracking, abbreviated to *Minitrack*.

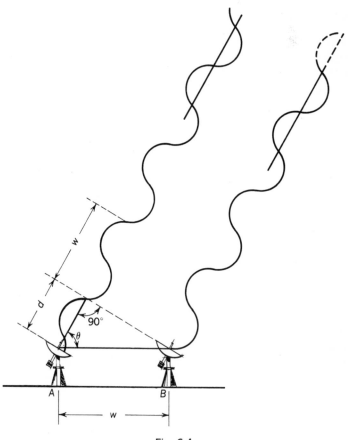

Fig. 6-4

The principle of the STADAN system is illustrated in Figure 6-4. The satellite transmits a continuous radio signal with wavelength w. For a 136 megacycle signal, w is about 7 feet. Two ground antennas are placed at A and B separated by the distance w. The angle of the satellite signals, indicating the direction of the satellite, is θ. When the satellite is at the right of the receiving antenna, as indicated in the figure, the radio signal will reach A later than B, since it must travel the extra distance d. The distance d is measured electrically by means of the phase delay between the signals at the two antennas. Knowing d and w, we can compute the ratio $\dfrac{d}{w}$, which is the cosine of the angle θ. We can then look up the number of degrees in the angle by using a table of cosines.

Suppose that a satellite is transmitting a 136 megacycle signal with a wavelength of seven feet. Our receiving equipment shows that d is five feet. Then $\cos \theta = \dfrac{5}{7} = .714$. We find from a table of cosines that the smallest angle with a cosine of .714 contains $44° 35'$. That is, the satellite is somewhere in a plane which makes an angle of 44 degrees 35 minutes with the Earth's surface. If now we have a second set of antennas placed perpendicular to the first set, we can locate the satellite in another plane intersecting the first plane and thus locate precisely the line of sight to the satellite.

Space Flights

6-15. A radio signal travels with the speed of light, 186,300 miles per second. A 136 megacycle signal has 136,000,000 cycles per second. The length of one cycle, from one crest to the next crest, is the length of one wavelength. Find the distance in feet that light travels per second and divide by the number of wavelengths per second to verify that one wavelength is about seven feet long.

6-16. The operator finds that there is no phase delay between the signals reaching A and B, and therefore d equals 0. What do we know about the location of the satellite?

6-17. If the distance d is 3½ feet, what is the angle of inclination of the plane in which the satellite is moving? (The angle can be found by geometrical relationships without reference to a table of cosines.)

6-18. The radio signal reaches B later than it reaches A. What do we know immediately about the location of the satellite?

Effects of Relativity

Man is just at the beginning of the space age, and his exploration of space to date has been limited to areas near the Earth. There is no reason to believe that the curiosity of man will be satisfied by the successful exploration of space around the Earth and the Moon only. Man will want to explore the entire Solar System and eventually other star systems. A space technology advanced far beyond that achieved at the present time will be needed. Flights into deep space may require periods of many years. It is interesting to speculate about the possibilities that may be present when sources of propulsion and life-support systems have been developed which will make trips lasting many years possible.

Suppose that a long-lasting source of propulsion has been developed which will give a spacecraft an acceleration of one-fifth g, or about six feet per second per second. What velocity would the spacecraft achieve within five years? By formula (2) the velocity reached in miles per second would be $\frac{6 \times 5 \times 365 \times 24 \times 3600}{5280} = 179,000$. The craft at the end of five years would be traveling at almost the speed of light, and at the end of six years would be considerably exceeding the speed of light. The remaining distance to Proxima Centauri, the nearest star, could be covered in less than two more years. But now we must consider what happens to a body when it moves at such speeds with reference to another body.

Einstein's Theory of Relativity says that if m is the mass of a body at rest, then if the body moves with reference to another body, the mass m' of the moving body is determined by the following equation, in which v is the velocity of the moving body and c is the velocity of light:

$$m' = \frac{m}{\sqrt{1 - \dfrac{v^2}{c^2}}} \qquad (50)$$

We can see at a glance that if $v = 0$ (that is, the body has no velocity and remains at rest), the value of the fraction $\dfrac{v^2}{c^2}$ is $\dfrac{0}{c^2} = 0$, the denominator is $\sqrt{1} = 1$, and therefore $m' = m$. That is, there is no change in mass. If v increases, the value under the radical sign becomes less than one, making the denominator less than one, and m' is then greater than m. Therefore, the velocity of the moving body has produced an increase in its mass. (If an increase in velocity increases mass, then it would appear that a man who runs for exercise in order to lose weight is defeating his own purpose. When he is running, his weight is greater than it was before.) What will happen when a body is moving with the speed of light, so that $v = c$? If v could equal c, the ratio $\dfrac{v^2}{c^2}$ would equal 1, and the number under the radical sign would equal $1 - 1 = 0$. The equation then reduces to $m' = \dfrac{m}{0}$. What is the meaning of $\dfrac{m}{0}$? We learn in advanced mathematics that if the denominator of a fraction becomes smaller and smaller and approaches zero, while the numerator is a real number not equal to 0, the value of the fraction grows beyond all bound and approaches infinity as a limit. Thus $\dfrac{m}{0} = m'$ would represent an infinitely large number. This result means if the velocity of a body could equal the speed of light, its mass would become infinitely large, and an infinitely large force would be required to accelerate it further. If all of the forces in the entire universe could be combined we would still not have an infinitely large force. It is apparent that the speed of light is the limiting speed for all objects in the Universe.

Find the speed which will just double the mass of a moving body.

Then $m' = 2m$, or

$$2m = \frac{m}{\sqrt{1 - \dfrac{v^2}{c^2}}}$$

Simplifying,

$$\sqrt{1 - \frac{v^2}{c^2}} = \tfrac{1}{2}$$

$$1 - \frac{v^2}{c^2} = \tfrac{1}{4}$$

$$\frac{v^2}{c^2} = \tfrac{3}{4}$$

$$v = \sqrt{3 \frac{c^2}{4}} = \sqrt{3 \left(\frac{c}{2}\right)}$$

Therefore,

$$v = 1.73 \left(\frac{186{,}300}{2}\right) = 161{,}000.$$

When the velocity of the moving body reaches 161,000 miles per second, its mass will be double its mass when at rest.

The theory of relativity points out rather interesting consequences of motion. If l is the length of a body at rest, its apparent length l' when it is moving with reference to another body is expressed by the equation

$$l' = l\sqrt{1 - \frac{v^2}{c^2}}. \tag{51}$$

In this case the radical is not in the denominator, but is a multiplier of l. It is apparent that the length of the moving body appears to *decrease* as its velocity increases. We found in the previous example that the value of the radical is $\tfrac{1}{2}$ when $v = 161{,}000$. Assume that the moving body is a spacecraft moving with relation to the Earth. Therefore, when the spacecraft reaches a velocity of 161,000 miles per second, it will appear to an observer on Earth to have shrunk to one-half of its original length. If its velocity could reach the speed of light, the spacecraft would appear to an observer on Earth to have length zero—it would have disappeared. This result seems to agree with what we would have intuitively expected. If the spacecraft were moving away from us with the speed of light, then light from the craft would never reach us and there would be no means by which we could see it or know of its existence. To those on board the spacecraft, however, no change would be apparent and life for them would be proceeding as usual.

An even more interesting result predicted by Einstein is the dilation of time. If t is the time required for a process in a moving system, then the process will appear to observers in the other system to take time t' as expressed in the following equation:

$$t' = \frac{t}{\sqrt{1 - \dfrac{v^2}{c^2}}} \tag{52}$$

As the velocity of the moving system increases, the time t' as measured by observers in the other system will be greater than it appears to be to persons in the moving system. If the velocity of the moving system, a spacecraft for example, approached the speed of light, the time as measured by the observers in the other system, on Earth for example, would seem to become infinitely long. Or, from another viewpoint, if the time is measured by the Earth observers with standard Earth clocks, indicating to them a normal passage of time, the clocks in the moving system, the spacecraft, would appear to move much more slowly so that their time would seem to be very short.

This change in time between the two systems is the source of the so-called "twin paradox." Suppose that one of two twin brothers leaves the Earth on a spacecraft and travels for many years at a speed approaching the speed of light. Time changes very slowly for the traveling twin, while it changes at the regular rate for the twin who remained on Earth. When the traveling twin returns to Earth, he may have aged by only a few minutes, while the twin who remained on Earth may be an old man. If the traveling twin had married and had children before beginning his trip, he may find upon his return to Earth that his children are much older than he is. It has been suggested by some persons that traveling in space may be the key to eternal youth. However, experts in the Theory of Relativity tell us that the above effect could not actually occur. The formula applies only when the relative velocity is constant. In the case of the above twins, the difference in times in the two systems is wiped out when the spacecraft is accelerating and decelerating during take-off and landing.

Space Flights

6-19. Find the velocity at which the mass of a moving body will be multiplied by four.

6-20. Find the velocity at which the mass of a moving body will be multiplied by 10.

Summary of Equations and Formulas

(1) $v_a = \dfrac{s}{t}$

(2) $v = at$

(3) $s = v_a t$

(4) $s = \frac{1}{2} a t^2$

(5) $s = \dfrac{v^2}{2a}$

(6) $v^2 = 2as$

(7) $f = ma$

(8) $f = \dfrac{w}{g} a$

(9) $a = \dfrac{fg}{w}$

(10) $F = \dfrac{m v^2}{r}$

(11) $m = \dfrac{w}{g}$

(12) $F = \dfrac{w v^2}{gr}$

(13) $F = G \dfrac{M m}{d^2}$

(14) $w_h = \left(\dfrac{r}{r+h}\right)^2 w_s$

(15) $g_h = \left(\dfrac{r}{r+h}\right)^2 g_s$

(16) $d = \sqrt{1.5 h_f}$

(17) $P = (14.7) \left(\frac{1}{2}\right)^{\frac{A}{3\frac{1}{4}}}$

(18) $\dfrac{P^2}{p^2} = \dfrac{D^3}{d^3}$

(19) $E = mc^2$

(20) Distance in parsecs $= \dfrac{1}{p''}$

(21) $f = \dfrac{w}{t\,g} c$

(22) $f = \dfrac{w}{t\,g} c + (P_e - P_a)\, A_e$

(23) $a = g \left(\dfrac{f}{w} - 1\right)$

(24) $s = \dfrac{v^2}{2g}$

(25) $H = h + \dfrac{v^2}{2g}$

(26) $I_s = \dfrac{f t}{w} = \dfrac{f}{w/t}$

(27) $I_s = \dfrac{c}{g}$

(28) $I_t = I_s w$

(29) $I_t = ft$

(30) $v = c \log_e R$

(31) $v = c \log_e R - gt$

(32) $v = c_1 \log_e R_1 + c_2 \log_e R_2 + c_3 \log_e R_3$

(33) $t = \sqrt{\dfrac{2 s}{g}}$

(34) $v = \sqrt{\dfrac{G M}{r}}$

(35) $v = \sqrt{\dfrac{9.56\,(10^1)}{r}}$

(36) $v = \sqrt{\dfrac{g R^2}{r}}$

(37) $e = \dfrac{c}{a} = \dfrac{\sqrt{a^2 - b^2}}{a}$

(38) $a = \frac{1}{2}(A + P)$

(39) $c = \frac{1}{2}(A - P)$

(40) $e = \dfrac{A - P}{A + P}$

(41) $v_A = \sqrt{\dfrac{GM}{A}(1 - e)}$

(42) $v_P = \sqrt{\dfrac{GM}{P}(1 + e)}$

(43) $\dfrac{v_A}{v_P} = \dfrac{P}{A}$

(44) $p_c = 2\pi \sqrt{\dfrac{r^3}{GM}}$

(45) $p_e = 2\pi \sqrt{\dfrac{a^3}{GM}}$

(46) $v = \sqrt{GM \left(\dfrac{2}{r} - \dfrac{1}{a}\right)}$

(47) $v = \sqrt{\dfrac{2\,GM}{r}}$

(48) $R = \rho\, A v^2$

(49) $N = \dfrac{1}{2\,\pi} \sqrt{\dfrac{a}{r}}$

(50) $m' = \dfrac{m}{\sqrt{1 - \dfrac{v^2}{c^2}}}$

(51) $l' = l \sqrt{1 - \dfrac{v^2}{c^2}}$

(52) $t' = \dfrac{t}{\sqrt{1 - \dfrac{v^2}{c^2}}}$

Answers to Space Flights

A generally accepted rule for computation when approximate numbers obtained by measurement are involved is that the answer is no more accurate than the least accurate item in the data. That is, the final answer should generally be rounded to the least number of significant digits found in the data. The application of this rule requires that most of the answers to problems in this book be rounded to not more than three significant digits.

1–1. 3 miles per hour per sec.; 4.4 ft. per sec. per sec.

1–2. 6.6 ft. per sec. per sec.; 330 ft.

1–3. 5.87 ft. per sec. per sec.; 188 ft.

1–4. 177.4 lb.; 160 lb.

1–5. 4.45 ft. per sec. per sec.; 6.38 ft. per sec. per sec.

1–6. zero lb.

1–7. 7.88 sec.; 254 ft. per sec.

1–8. 7.86 ft. per sec. per sec.

1–9. 11.1 min.

1–10. 43.2 sec. or .0120 hour; 6 miles

1–11. 49.4 sec.

1–12. 32.2 ft. per sec. per sec.; 322 ft. per sec.

1–13. 12.9 ft. per sec.

1–14. 0.78 lb.

1–15. 1.63 ft.

1–16. Let $F_1 = \dfrac{wv^2}{gr} \cdot F_2 = \dfrac{w(2v)^2}{g(2r)} = 2\,\dfrac{wv^2}{gr} = 2F_1$

1–17. $F = .95\,w$

1–18. 20.07 lb.

1–19. $.0227\,w$

1–20. 3630 lb.

1–21. Reduced to ⅙ of its surface weight.

1–22. 2.01 ft. per sec. per sec.

1–23. $\dfrac{1}{300}$ lb., resulting in an error of about .3 percent

1–24. The weight with reference to either the Earth or the Moon is $.00034\,w$.

1–25. $.95\,w$

2–1.   63,200 A.U.
2–2. 1.92×10^{12} miles
2–3.   93,000,000 miles
2–4.   .00257 A.U.
2–5.   21,600 nautical miles
2–6.   29.3 light years; 23.8 light years
2–7.   6.44 parsecs; .307 parsecs
2–8.   .8 mach
2–9.   2750 ft. per sec.; 1875 miles per hr.; 1628 nautical miles per hr. (knots)
2–10. 510 lb.
2–11. 6.21 g or 6.21 times his normal weight
2–12. .27 g
2–13. 10 g
2–14. 216 ft. per sec. per sec.; 248 ft. per sec. per sec.
2–15. 11,900 ft. per sec. or 8110 miles per hr.
2–16. 1230 lb.
2–17. 119 ft. per sec. per sec.
2–18. 4.3 degrees
2–19. 15 miles; 38.7 miles; 89 miles
2–20. 1030 miles
2–21. 6 miles
2–22. $\dfrac{15}{22}$; $\dfrac{22}{15}$

3–1.   1.06 tons
3–2.   1060 lb. or .53 tons
3–3.   4.82 lb. per sq. in.
3–4. 5.81×10^{15} tons
3–5.   oxygen 3.43 lb. per sq. in.; hydrogen 11.13 lb. per sq. in.
3–6.   21.8 miles
3–7.   13.7 lb. per sq. in.
3–8.   8.7 lb. per sq. in.
3–9.   3.43 lb. per sq. in. (See 3–5.)
3–10. 6.94 miles or about 37,000 ft.
3–11. 21 percent by volume, 23.3 percent by weight
3–12. .86 lb. per sq. in.
3–13. .027 lb. per sq. in.
3–14. 13,000 lb.
3–15. 1.27 lb. per sq. in.
3–16. Increased 46 percent
3–17. 52 miles per sec.

3–18. 1 mile per sec. (meteorite overtaking spacecraft)

3–19. 4400

3–20. Along Earth's geomagnetic axis, or in general over the North or South Pole

3–21. Least exposure: 100 miles; 50,000 miles; 7 Earth radii
Most exposure: 18,000 miles; 8,500 miles

3–22. 99.9 percent

3–23. Jupiter and Mercury

3–24. Venus

3–25. Mercury

3–26. There is a perfect correspondence between distance from Sun and period of revolution, the period increasing as the distance increases.

3–27. 8.32 min.

3–28. 2.50 sec.

3–29. $d = 3\sqrt{\dfrac{h_f}{22}}$

3–30. 6.4 miles; 356 miles

3–31. Velocity in miles per sec.: Mercury 29.7; Mars 14.9; Uranus 4.22; Neptune 3.37. Orbital velocity decreases as the radius increases.

3–32. Jupiter: $P^2 = 142$, $D^3 = 141$; Saturn: $P^2 = 870$, $D^3 = 866$

3–33. $\dfrac{F_m}{F_e} = \dfrac{(.11)\,M\,(1)}{(2100)^2} \times \dfrac{(3960)^2}{M\,(1)} = \dfrac{1.725 \times 10^6}{4.41 \times 10^6}$
$= .39$; $.39 \times 32.2 = 12.6$ ft. per sec. per sec.

3–34. Acceleration in ft. per sec. per sec.: Earth 32.2; Jupiter 85.0; Mars 12.6; Mercury 8.37; Neptune 36.1; Saturn 34.5; Uranus 29.3; Venus 27.7

3–35. $\dfrac{F_s}{F_e} = \dfrac{(95)\,M\,(1)}{(37,250)^2} \times \dfrac{(3960)^2}{M\,(1)} = 1.07$

3–36. Velocity in ft. per sec.: Moon 54.7; Mars 126; Neptune 361; Jupiter 850

3–37. Moon 9850 ft.; Mars 22,700 ft.; Neptune 65,000 ft.

3–38. Mars 9.1 ft.; Neptune 5.8 ft.; Jupiter 4.8 ft.

3–39. Moon 340 ft.-lb.; Mars 780 ft.-lb.; Saturn 2140 ft.-lb.; Venus 1720 ft.-lb.

3–40. Moon 78.5 ft.; Jupiter 8.8 ft.

3–41. 123 lb.

3–42. 725 lb.

3–43. Moon 24.3 ft.; Venus 8.02 ft.

3–44. 162,000 miles from center of Earth

3–45. 8,724,000 miles from center of Mars

3–46. 20,040,000 miles from center of Neptune
3–47. 81,500 light years; 4.8×10^{17} miles
3–48. 8000 parsecs; 26,100 light years; 1.54×10^{17} miles
3–49. 1.32 parsecs; 4.30 light years; 2.53×10^{13} miles
3–50. .38 seconds
3–51. 200 parsecs; 652 light years; 3.84×10^{15} miles
3–52. .123 seconds
3–53. .38 seconds
3–54. 143 parsecs; .007 seconds
3–55. 10 lb.

4–1. 1.04 ounce
4–2. 3885 lb.; 3956 lb.
4–3. 42.6 lb. per sec.
4–4. 3580 ft. per sec.
4–5. 7250 ft.; 483 ft. per sec.; 10,900 ft.
4–6. 2420 ft.; 483 ft. per sec.; 6040 ft.
       21,700 ft.; 1450 ft. per sec.; 54,400 ft.
4–7. $a = 0$ or $a < 0$. There is no lift.
4–8. 3930 ft.; 472 ft. per sec.
4–9. 2.25
4–10. 2
4–11. 12.5 sec.
4–12. 1.23
4–13. 2,580 ft. per sec.; 58,000 ft.
4–14. 1.24
4–15. *gt*
4–16. Exhaust velocities in ft. per sec.; 9210; 12,500; 12,800;
       8,310; 7,410; 25,800; 25,800 to 48,300; 113,000 to 483,000.
4–17. 900 lb.
4–18. 1350 lb-sec.
4–19. 57,200,000 lb.-sec.; 191,000 lb.; 4.42 lb.
4–20. .0067 lb.
4–21. 188 sec.
4–22. 194 sec.
4–23. 172,300 lb.-sec.
4–24. 162 sec.; 431 sec.; total 593 sec.
4–25. 168 sec.; 354 sec.; 446 sec.; total 968 sec.
4–26. 1,701,000,000 lb.-sec.
4–27. 14,700 ft. per sec.; 4,237,000 ft. or 802 miles
4–28. 14.3
4–29. 2750 ft. per sec.; 61,800 ft.

4–30. 8440 ft. per sec.; 177,000 ft.; 1,283,000 ft. or 243 miles

4–31. 5650 ft. per sec.; 119,000 ft.; 614,000 ft. or 116 miles

4–32. 20,000 miles per hour, which is greater than orbital velocity

4–33. 27,500 miles per hour, which is greater than escape velocity

5–1. 2.79 sec.

5–2. .61 sec.; 1220 ft.

5–3. 16.1 ft.; 48.3 ft.; 80.5 ft.; 112.7 ft.; 144.9 ft.

5–4. 18.1 sec.

5–5. 15,700 miles per hr.; 119 min.

5–6. 35.0 min.

5–7. 91.2 min.

5–8. 81.0 min.

5–9. 3600 miles per hr.; 119 min.

5–10. None

5–11. $gR^2 = \dfrac{32.2}{5280} (3960)^2 = (9.56)(10^4)$

5–12. 8807 hours or 367 days (More precise data would give the true period of 365¼ days.)

5–13.

Altitude (Miles above surface)	Velocity (Miles per hour)	Period
0	17,600	85 min.
100	17,500	86 min.
500	16,700	101 min.
1,000	15,700	119 min.
22,300	6,880	24 hours
37,700	5,450	48 hours
235,000	2,280	27.4 days

5–14. 42.4 percent

5–15. .140; 4860 miles; 4810 miles

5–16. .820; 868 miles per hr.: 8750 miles per hr.

5–17. .010

5–18. 10,400 miles; 1680 miles; .436

5–19. .937; 24,260 miles per hr.; 785 miles per hr.; 3750 miles per hr.

5–20. 163 miles

5–21. 5290 ft. per sec.

5–22. $e = .773$; $P = 3362$; perigee $= -598$. Syncom would have fallen toward Earth on the side opposite apogee, burning up in the atmosphere.

5–23. $\dfrac{\sqrt{\dfrac{GM}{A}(1-e)}}{\sqrt{\dfrac{GM}{P}(1+e)}} = \dfrac{P}{A}$

5–24. $v_A = 0$. This condition could exist only when $A = \infty$, meaning that the orbit is open instead of closed, and a velocity perpendicular to a radial line to the focus does not exist.

5–25. $A = 2P$; $A = nP$. As n increases, the ellipse becomes elongated and the eccentricity increases.

5–26.

Altitude (Miles above surface)	Escape Velocity (Miles per hour)
500	23,600
1,000	22,200
22,300	9,700
37,700	7,700
235,000	3,220

5–27. 7880 miles per hr.; 106 min.; 11,100 miles per hr.

5–28. 16,100 miles per hr.; 91 min.; 22,700 miles per hr.

5–29. .0216

5–30. Escape velocity in miles per sec.: 3.2; 1.57; 1.5; 22

6–1. zero

6–2. Becomes ¼ as great

6–3. 9.7 ft. per sec.

6–4. 51.6 lb.

6–5. None. It will remain in orbit.

6–6. 1.90 ft. per sec.

6–7. 28.2 ft. per sec. per sec.

6–8. 2.42 per minute

6–9. 2.42 per minute; 30.9 ft. per sec. per sec.

6–10. 1.91 per min.

6–11. 25,500 miles per hr.; 14,800,000 miles

6–12. 23,800 miles per hr.; 1,890,000 miles
       27,400 miles per hr.; 49,200,000 miles

6–13. 569,000 miles per hr.

6–14. 74.5 sec.

6–15. 7.23 ft.

6–16. In a vertical plane

6–17. 60 degrees

6–18. To the left of the station

6–19. 180,400 miles per sec.

6–20. 185,400 miles per sec.

1 — Powers, Roots, Reciprocals — 50

N	N^2	$\sqrt{N}$	$\sqrt{10N}$	N^3	$\sqrt[3]{N}$	$\sqrt[3]{10N}$	$\sqrt[3]{100N}$	$1000/N$
1	1	1.00 000	3.16 228	1	1.00 000	2.15 443	4.64 159	1000.00
2	4	1.41 421	4.47 214	8	1.25 992	2.71 442	5.84 804	500.00 0
3	9	1.73 205	5.47 723	27	1.44 225	3.10 723	6.69 433	333.33 3
4	16	2.00 000	6.32 456	64	1.58 740	3.41 995	7.36 806	250.00 0
5	25	2.23 607	7.07 107	125	1.70 998	3.68 403	7.93 701	200.00 0
6	36	2.44 949	7.74 597	216	1.81 712	3.91 487	8.43 433	166.66 7
7	49	2.64 575	8.36 660	343	1.91 293	4.12 129	8.87 904	142.85 7
8	64	2.82 843	8.94 427	512	2.00 000	4.30 887	9.28 318	125.00 0
9	81	3.00 000	9.48 683	729	2.08 008	4.48 140	9.65 489	111.11 1
10	100	3.16 228	10.00 00	1 000	2.15 443	4.64 159	10.00 00	100.00 0
11	121	3.31 662	10.48 81	1 331	2.22 398	4.79 142	10.32 28	90.90 91
12	144	3.46 410	10.95 45	1 728	2.28 943	4.93 242	10.62 66	83.33 33
13	169	3.60 555	11.40 18	2 197	2.35 133	5.06 580	10.91 39	76.92 31
14	196	3.74 166	11.83 22	2 744	2.41 014	5.19 249	11.18 69	71.42 86
15	225	3.87 298	12.24 74	3 375	2.46 621	5.31 329	11.44 71	66.66 67
16	256	4.00 000	12.64 91	4 096	2.51 984	5.42 884	11.69 61	62.50 00
17	289	4.12 311	13.03 84	4 913	2.57 128	5.53 966	11.93 48	58.82 35
18	324	4.24 264	13.41 64	5 832	2.62 074	5.64 622	12.16 44	55.55 56
19	361	4.35 890	13.78 40	6 859	2.66 840	5.74 890	12.38 56	52.63 16
20	400	4.47 214	14.14 21	8 000	2.71 442	5.84 804	12.59 92	50.00 00
21	441	4.58 258	14.49 14	9 261	2.75 892	5.94 392	12.80 58	47.61 90
22	484	4.69 042	14.83 24	10 648	2.80 204	6.03 681	13.00 59	45.45 45
23	529	4.79 583	15.16 58	12 167	2.84 387	6.12 693	13.20 01	43.47 83
24	576	4.89 898	15.49 19	13 824	2.88 450	6.21 446	13.38 87	41.66 67
25	625	5.00 000	15.81 14	15 625	2.92 402	6.29 961	13.57 21	40.00 00
26	676	5.09 902	16.12 45	17 576	2.96 250	6.38 250	13.75 07	38.46 15
27	729	5.19 615	16.43 17	19 683	3.00 000	6.46 330	13.92 48	37.03 70
28	784	5.29 150	16.73 32	21 952	3.03 659	6.54 213	14.09 46	35.71 43
29	841	5.38 516	17.02 94	24 389	3.07 232	6.61 911	14.26 04	34.48 28
30	900	5.47 723	17.32 05	27 000	3.10 723	6.69 433	14.42 25	33.33 33
31	961	5.56 776	17.60 68	29 791	3.14 138	6.76 790	14.58 10	32.25 81
32	1 024	5.65 685	17.88 85	32 768	3.17 480	6.83 990	14.73 61	31.25 00
33	1 089	5.74 456	18.16 59	35 937	3.20 753	6.91 042	14.88 81	30.30 30
34	1 156	5.83 095	18.43 91	39 304	3.23 961	6.97 953	15.03 69	29.41 18
35	1 225	5.91 608	18.70 83	42 875	3.27 107	7.04 730	15.18 29	28.57 14
36	1 296	6.00 000	18.97 37	46 656	3.30 193	7.11 379	15.32 62	27.77 78
37	1 369	6.08 276	19.23 54	50 653	3.33 222	7.17 905	15.46 68	27.02 70
38	1 444	6.16 441	19.49 36	54 872	3.36 198	7.24 316	15.60 49	26.31 58
39	1 521	6.24 500	19.74 84	59 319	3.39 121	7.30 614	15.74 06	25.64 10
40	1 600	6.32 456	20.00 00	64 000	3.41 995	7.36 806	15.87 40	25.00 00
41	1 681	6.40 312	20.24 85	68 921	3.44 822	7.42 896	16.00 52	24.39 02
42	1 764	6.48 074	20.49 39	74 088	3.47 603	7.48 887	16.13 43	23.80 95
43	1 849	6.55 744	20.73 64	79 507	3.50 340	7.54 784	16.26 13	23.25 58
44	1 936	6.63 325	20.97 62	85 184	3.53 035	7.60 590	16.38 64	22.72 73
45	2 025	6.70 820	21.21 32	91 125	3.55 689	7.66 309	16.50 96	22.22 22
46	2 116	6.78 233	21.44 76	97 336	3.58 305	7.71 944	16.63 10	21.73 91
47	2 209	6.85 565	21.67 95	103 823	3.60 883	7.77 498	16.75 07	21.27 66
48	2 304	6.92 820	21.90 89	110 592	3.63 424	7.82 974	16.86 87	20.83 33
49	2 401	7.00 000	22.13 59	117 649	3.65 931	7.88 374	16.98 50	20.40 82
50	2 500	7.07 107	22.36 07	125 000	3.68 403	7.93 701	17.09 98	20.00 00
N	N^2	$\sqrt{N}$	$\sqrt{10N}$	N^3	$\sqrt[3]{N}$	$\sqrt[3]{10N}$	$\sqrt[3]{100N}$	$1000/N$

134

50 — Powers, Roots, Reciprocals — 100

N	N²	√N	√10N	N³	∛N	∛10N	∛100N	1000/N
50	2 500	7.07 107	22.36 07	125 000	3.68 403	7.93 701	17.09 98	20.00 00
51	2 601	7.14 143	22.58 32	132 651	3.70 843	7.98 957	17.21 30	19.60 78
52	2 704	7.21 110	22.80 35	140 608	3.73 251	8.04 145	17.32 48	19.23 08
53	2 809	7.28 011	23.02 17	148 877	3.75 629	8.09 267	17.43 51	18.86 79
54	2 916	7.34 847	23.23 79	157 464	3.77 976	8.14 325	17.54 41	18.51 85
55	3 025	7.41 620	23.45 21	166 375	3.80 295	8.19 321	17.65 17	18.18 18
56	3 136	7.48 331	23.66 43	175 616	3.82 586	8.24 257	17.75 81	17.85 71
57	3 249	7.54 983	23.87 47	185 193	3.84 850	8.29 134	17.86 32	17.54 39
58	3 364	7.61 577	24.08 32	195 112	3.87 088	8.33 955	17.96 70	17.24 14
59	3 481	7.68 115	24.28 99	205 379	3.89 300	8.38 721	18.06 97	16.94 92
60	3 600	7.74 597	24.49 49	216 000	3.91 487	8.43 433	18.17 12	16.66 67
61	3 721	7.81 025	24.69 82	226 981	3.93 650	8.48 093	18.27 16	16.39 34
62	3 844	7.87 401	24.89 98	238 328	3.95 789	8.52 702	18.37 09	16.12 90
63	3 969	7.93 725	25.09 98	250 047	3.97 906	8.57 262	18.46 91	15.87 30
64	4 096	8.00 000	25.29 82	262 144	4.00 000	8.61 774	18.56 64	15.62 50
65	4 225	8.06 226	25.49 51	274 625	4.02 073	8.66 239	18.66 26	15.38 46
66	4 356	8.12 404	25.69 05	287 496	4.04 124	8.70 659	18.75 78	15.15 15
67	4 489	8.18 535	25.88 44	300 763	4.06 155	8.75 034	18.85 20	14.92 54
68	4 624	8.24 621	26.07 68	314 432	4.08 166	8.79 366	18.94 54	14.70 59
69	4 761	8.30 662	26.26 79	328 509	4.10 157	8.83 656	19.03 78	14.49 28
70	4 900	8.36 660	26.45 75	343 000	4.12 129	8.87 904	19.12 93	14.28 57
71	5 041	8.42 615	26.64 58	357 911	4.14 082	8.92 112	19.22 00	14.08 45
72	5 184	8.48 528	26.83 28	373 248	4.16 017	8.96 281	19.30 98	13.88 89
73	5 329	8.54 400	27.01 85	389 017	4.17 934	9.00 411	19.39 88	13.69 86
74	5 476	8.60 233	27.20 29	405 224	4.19 834	9.04 504	19.48 70	13.51 35
75	5 625	8.66 025	27.38 61	421 875	4.21 716	9.08 560	19.57 43	13.33 33
76	5 776	8.71 780	27.56 81	438 976	4.23 582	9.12 581	19.66 10	13.15 79
77	5 929	8.77 496	27.74 89	456 533	4.25 432	9.16 566	19.74 68	12.98 70
78	6 084	8.83 176	27.92 85	474 552	4.27 266	9.20 516	19.83 19	12.82 05
79	6 241	8.88 819	28.10 69	493 039	4.29 084	9.24 434	19.91 63	12.65 82
80	6 400	8.94 427	28.28 43	512 000	4.30 887	9.28 318	20.00 00	12.50 00
81	6 561	9.00 000	28.46 05	531 441	4.32 675	9.32 170	20.08 30	12.34 57
82	6 724	9.05 539	28.63 56	551 368	4.34 448	9.35 990	20.16 53	12.19 51
83	6 889	9.11 043	28.80 97	571 787	4.36 207	9.39 780	20.24 69	12.04 82
84	7 056	9.16 515	28.98 28	592 704	4.37 952	9.43 539	20.32 79	11.90 48
85	7 225	9.21 954	29.15 48	614 125	4.39 683	9.47 268	20.40 83	11.76 47
86	7 396	9.27 362	29.32 58	636 056	4.41 400	9.50 969	20.48 80	11.62 79
87	7 569	9.32 738	29.49 58	658 503	4.43 105	9.54 640	20.56 71	11.49 43
88	7 744	9.38 083	29.66 48	681 472	4.44 796	9.58 284	20.64 56	11.36 36
89	7 921	9.43 398	29.83 29	704 969	4.46 475	9.61 900	20.72 35	11.23 60
90	8 100	9.48 683	30.00 00	729 000	4.48 140	9.65 489	20.80 08	11.11 11
91	8 281	9.53 939	30.16 62	753 571	4.49 794	9.69 052	20.87 76	10.98 90
92	8 464	9.59 166	30.33 15	778 688	4.51 436	9.72 589	20.95 38	10.86 96
93	8 649	9.64 365	30.49 59	804 357	4.53 065	9.76 100	21.02 94	10.75 27
94	8 836	9.69 536	30.65 94	830 584	4.54 684	9.79 586	21.10 45	10.63 83
95	9 025	9.74 679	30.82 21	857 375	4.56 290	9.83 048	21.17 91	10.52 63
96	9 216	9.79 796	30.98 39	884 736	4.57 886	9.86 485	21.25 32	10.41 67
97	9 409	9.84 886	31.14 48	912 673	4.59 470	9.89 898	21.32 67	10.30 93
98	9 604	9.89 949	31.30 50	941 192	4.61 044	9.93 288	21.39 97	10.20 41
99	9 801	9.94 987	31.46 43	970 299	4.62 607	9.96 655	21.47 23	10.10 10
100	10 000	10.00 000	31.62 28	1 000 000	4.64 159	10.00 000	21.54 43	10.00 00
N	N²	√N	√10N	N³	∛N	∛10N	∛100N	1000/N

100 — Powers, Roots, Reciprocals — 150

N	N^2	$\sqrt{N}$	$\sqrt{10N}$	N^3	$\sqrt[3]{N}$	$\sqrt[3]{10N}$	$\sqrt[3]{100N}$	$1000/N$
100	10 000	10.00 00	31.62 28	1 000 000	4.64 159	10.00 00	21.54 43	10.00 000
101	10 201	10.04 99	31.78 05	1 030 301	4.65 701	10.03 32	21.61 59	9.90 099
102	10 404	10.09 95	31.93 74	1 061 208	4.67 233	10.06 62	21.68 70	9.80 392
103	10 609	10.14 89	32.09 36	1 092 727	4.68 755	10.09 90	21.75 77	9.70 874
104	10 816	10.19 80	32.24 90	1 124 864	4.70 267	10.13 16	21.82 79	9.61 538
105	11 025	10.24 70	32.40 37	1 157 625	4.71 769	10.16 40	21.89 76	9.52 381
106	11 236	10.29 56	32.55 76	1 191 016	4.73 262	10.19 61	21.96 69	9.43 396
107	11 449	10.34 41	32.71 09	1 225 043	4.74 746	10.22 81	22.03 58	9.34 579
108	11 664	10.39 23	32.86 34	1 259 712	4.76 220	10.25 99	22.10 42	9.25 926
109	11 881	10.44 03	33.01 51	1 295 029	4.77 686	10.29 14	22.17 22	9.17 431
110	12 100	10.48 81	33.16 62	1 331 000	4.79 142	10.32 28	22.23 98	9.09 091
111	12 321	10.53 57	33.31 67	1 367 631	4.80 590	10.35 40	22.30 70	9.00 901
112	12 544	10.58 30	33.46 64	1 404 928	4.82 028	10.38 50	22.37 38	8.92 857
113	12 769	10.63 01	33.61 55	1 442 897	4.83 459	10.41 58	22.44 02	8.84 956
114	12 996	10.67 71	33.76 39	1 481 544	4.84 881	10.44 64	22.50 62	8.77 193
115	13 225	10.72 38	33.91 16	1 520 875	4.86 294	10.47 69	22.57 18	8.69 565
116	13 456	10.77 03	34.05 88	1 560 896	4.87 700	10.50 72	22.63 70	8.62 069
117	13 689	10.81 67	34.20 53	1 601 613	4.89 097	10.53 73	22.70 19	8.54 701
118	13 924	10.86 28	34.35 11	1 643 032	4.90 487	10.56 72	22.76 64	8.47 458
119	14 161	10.90 87	34.49 64	1 685 159	4.91 868	10.59 70	22.83 05	8.40 336
120	14 400	10.95 45	34.64 10	1 728 000	4.93 242	10.62 66	22.89 43	8.33 333
121	14 641	11.00 00	34.78 51	1 771 561	4.94 609	10.65 60	22.95 77	8.26 446
122	14 884	11.04 54	34.92 85	1 815 848	4.95 968	10.68 53	23.02 08	8.19 672
123	15 129	11.09 05	35.07 14	1 860 867	4.97 319	10.71 44	23.08 35	8.13 008
124	15 376	11.13 55	35.21 36	1 906 624	4.98 663	10.74 34	23.14 59	8.06 452
125	15 625	11.18 03	35.35 53	1 953 125	5.00 000	10.77 22	23.20 79	8.00 000
126	15 876	11.22 50	35.49 65	2 000 376	5.01 330	10.80 08	23.26 97	7.93 651
127	16 129	11.26 94	35.63 71	2 048 383	5.02 653	10.82 93	23.33 11	7.87 402
128	16 384	11.31 37	35.77 71	2 097 152	5.03 968	10.85 77	23.39 21	7.81 250
129	16 641	11.35 78	35.91 66	2 146 689	5.05 277	10.88 59	23.45 29	7.75 194
130	16 900	11.40 18	36.05 55	2 197 000	5.06 580	10.91 39	23.51 33	7.69 231
131	17 161	11.44 55	36.19 39	2 248 091	5.07 875	10.94 18	23.57 35	7.63 359
132	17 424	11.48 91	36.33 18	2 299 968	5.09 164	10.96 96	23.63 33	7.57 576
133	17 689	11.53 26	36.46 92	2 352 637	5.10 447	10.99 72	23.69 28	7.51 880
134	17 956	11.57 58	36.60 60	2 406 104	5.11 723	11.02 47	23.75 21	7.46 269
135	18 225	11.61 90	36.74 23	2 460 375	5.12 993	11.05 21	23.81 10	7.40 741
136	18 496	11.66 19	36.87 82	2 515 456	5.14 256	11.07 93	23.86 97	7.35 294
137	18 769	11.70 47	37.01 35	2 571 353	5.15 514	11.10 64	23.92 80	7.29 927
138	19 044	11.74 73	37.14 84	2 628 072	5.16 765	11.13 34	23.98 61	7.24 638
139	19 321	11.78 98	37.28 27	2 685 619	5.18 010	11.16 02	24.04 39	7.19 424
140	19 600	11.83 22	37.41 66	2 744 000	5.19 249	11.18 69	24.10 14	7.14 286
141	19 881	11.87 43	37.55 00	2 803 221	5.20 483	11.21 35	24.15 87	7.09 220
142	20 164	11.91 64	37.68 29	2 863 288	5.21 710	11.23 99	24.21 56	7.04 225
143	20 449	11.95 83	37.81 53	2 924 207	5.22 932	11.26 62	24.27 24	6.99 301
144	20 736	12.00 00	37.94 73	2 985 984	5.24 148	11.29 24	24.32 88	6.94 444
145	21 025	12.04 16	38.07 89	3 048 625	5.25 359	11.31 85	24.38 50	6.89 655
146	21 316	12.08 30	38.20 99	3 112 136	5.26 564	11.34 45	24.44 09	6.84 932
147	21 609	12.12 44	38.34 06	3 176 523	5.27 763	11.37 03	24.49 66	6.80 272
148	21 904	12.16 55	38.47 08	3 241 792	5.28 957	11.39 60	24.55 20	6.75 676
149	22 201	12.20 66	38.60 05	3 307 949	5.30 146	11.42 16	24.60 72	6.71 141
150	22 500	12.24 74	38.72 98	3 375 000	5.31 329	11.44 71	24.66 21	6.66 667
N	N^2	$\sqrt{N}$	$\sqrt{10N}$	N^3	$\sqrt[3]{N}$	$\sqrt[3]{10N}$	$\sqrt[3]{100N}$	$1000/N$

136

N	N^2	$\sqrt{N}$	$\sqrt{10N}$	N^3	$\sqrt[3]{N}$	$\sqrt[3]{10N}$	$\sqrt[3]{100N}$	1000 /N
150	22 500	12.24 74	38.72 98	3 375 000	5.31 329	11.44 71	24.66 21	6.66 667
151	22 801	12.28 82	38.85 87	3 442 951	5.32 507	11.47 25	24.71 68	6.62 252
152	23 104	12.32 88	38.98 72	3 511 808	5.33 680	11.49 78	24.77 12	6.57 895
153	23 409	12.36 93	39.11 52	3 581 577	5.34 848	11.52 30	24.82 55	6.53 595
154	23 716	12.40 97	39.24 28	3 652 264	5.36 011	11.54 80	24.87 94	6.49 351
155	24 025	12.44 99	39.37 00	3 723 875	5.37 169	11.57 29	24.93 32	6.45 161
156	24 336	12.49 00	39.49 68	3 796 416	5.38 321	11.59 78	24.98 67	6.41 026
157	24 649	12.53 00	39.62 32	3 869 893	5.39 469	11.62 25	25.03 99	6.36 943
158	24 964	12.56 98	39.74 92	3 944 312	5.40 612	11.64 71	25.09 30	6.32 911
159	25 281	12.60 95	39.87 48	4 019 679	5.41 750	11.67 17	25.14 58	6.28 931
160	25 600	12.64 91	40.00 00	4 096 000	5.42 884	11.69 61	25.19 84	6.25 000
161	25 921	12.68 86	40.12 48	4 173 281	5.44 012	11.72 04	25.25 08	6.21 118
162	26 244	12.72 79	40.24 92	4 251 528	5.45 136	11.74 46	25.30 30	6.17 284
163	26 569	12.76 71	40.37 33	4 330 747	5.46 256	11.76 87	25.35 49	6.13 497
164	26 896	12.80 62	40.49 69	4 410 944	5.47 370	11.79 27	25.40 67	6.09 756
165	27 225	12.84 52	40.62 02	4 492 125	5.48 481	11.81 67	25.45 82	6.06 061
166	27 556	12.88 41	40.74 31	4.574 296	5.49 586	11.84 05	25.50 95	6.02 410
167	27 889	12.92 28	40.86 56	4 657 463	5.50 688	11.86 42	25.56 07	5.98 802
168	28 224	12.96 15	40.98 78	4 741 632	5.51 785	11.88 78	25.61 16	5.95 238
169	28 561	13.00 00	41.10 96	4 826 809	5.52 877	11.91 14	25.66 23	5.91 716
170	28 900	13.03 84	41.23 11	4 913 000	5.53 966	11.93 48	25.71 28	5.88 235
171	29 241	13.07 67	41.35 21	5 000 211	5.55 050	11.95 82	25.76 31	5.84 795
172	29 584	13.11 49	41.47 29	5 088 448	5.56 130	11.98 15	25.81 33	5.81 395
173	29 929	13.15 29	41.59 33	5 177 717	5.57 205	12.00 46	25.86 32	5.78 035
174	30 276	13.19 09	41.71 33	5 268 024	5.58 277	12.02 77	25.91 29	5.74 713
175	30 625	13.22 88	41.83 30	5 359 375	5.59 344	12.05 07	25.96 25	5.71 429
176	30 976	13.26 65	41.95 24	5 451 776	5.60 408	12.07 36	26.01 18	5.68 182
177	31 329	13.30 41	42.07 14	5 545 233	5.61 467	12.09 64	26.06 10	5.64 972
178	31 684	13.34 17	42.19 00	5 639 752	5.62 523	12.11 92	26.11 00	5.61 798
179	32 041	13.37 91	42.30 84	5 735 339	5.63 574	12.14 18	26.15 88	5.58 659
180	32 400	13.41 64	42.42 64	5 832 000	5.64 622	12.16 44	26.20 74	5.55 556
181	32 761	13.45 36	42.54 41	5 929 741	5.65 665	12.18 69	26.25 59	5.52 486
182	33 124	13.49 07	42.66 15	6 028 568	5.66 705	12.20 93	26.30 41	5.49 451
183	33 489	13.52 77	42.77 85	6 128 487	5.67 741	12.23 16	26.35 22	5.46 448
184	33 856	13.56 47	42.89 52	6 229 504	5.68 773	12.25 39	26.40 01	5.43 478
185	34 225	13.60 15	43.01 16	6 331 625	5.69 802	12.27 60	26.44 79	5.40 541
186	34 596	13.63 82	43.12 77	6 434 856	5.70 827	12.29 81	26.49 54	5.37 634
187	34 969	13.67 48	43.24 35	6 539 203	5.71 848	12.32 01	26.54 28	5.34 759
188	35 344	13.71 13	43.35 90	6 644 672	5.72 865	12.34 20	26.59 01	5.31 915
189	35 721	13.74 77	43.47 41	6 751 269	5.73 879	12.36 39	26.63 71	5.29 101
190	36 100	13.78 40	43.58 90	6 859 000	5.74 890	12.38 56	26.68 40	5.26 316
191	36 481	13.82 03	43.70 35	6 967 871	5.75 897	12.40 73	26.73 07	5.23 560
192	36 864	13.85 64	43.81 78	7 077 888	5.76 900	12.42 89	26.77 73	5.20 833
193	37 249	13.89 24	43.93 18	7 189 057	5.77 900	12.45 05	26.82 37	5.18 135
194	37 636	13.92 84	44.04 54	7 301 384	5.78 896	12.47 19	26.87 00	5.15 464
195	38 025	13.96 42	44.15 88	7 414 875	5.79 889	12.49 33	26.91 61	5.12 821
196	38 416	14.00 00	44.27 19	7 529 536	5.80 879	12.51 46	26.96 20	5.10 204
197	38 809	14.03 57	44.38 47	7 645 373	5.81 865	12.53 59	27.00 78	5.07 614
198	39 204	14.07 12	44.49 72	7 762 392	5.82 848	12.55 71	27.05 34	5.05 051
199	39 601	14.10 67	44.60 94	7 880 599	5.83 927	12.57 82	27.09 89	5.02 513
200	40 000	14.14 21	44.72 14	8 000 000	5.84 804	12.59 92	27.14 42	5.00 000
N	N^2	$\sqrt{N}$	$\sqrt{10N}$	N^3	$\sqrt[3]{N}$	$\sqrt[3]{10N}$	$\sqrt[3]{100N}$	1000 /N

200 — Powers, Roots, Reciprocals — 250

N	N^2	$\sqrt{N}$	$\sqrt{10N}$	N^3	$\sqrt[3]{N}$	$\sqrt[3]{10N}$	$\sqrt[3]{100N}$	$1000/N$
200	40 000	14.14 21	44.72 14	8 000 000	5.84 804	12.59 92	27.14 42	5.00 000
201	40 401	14.17 74	44.83 30	8 120 601	5.85 777	12.62 02	27.18 93	4.97 512
202	40 804	14.21 27	44.94 44	8 242 408	5.86 746	12.64 11	27.23 44	4.95 050
203	41 209	14.24 78	45.05 55	8 365 427	5.87 713	12.66 19	27.27 92	4.92 611
204	41 616	14.28 29	45.16 64	8 489 664	5.88 677	12.68 27	27.32 39	4.90 196
205	42 025	14.31 78	45.27 69	8 615 125	5.89 637	12.70 33	27.36 85	4.87 805
206	42 436	14.35 27	45.38 72	8 741 816	5.90 594	12.72 40	27.41 29	4.85 437
207	42 849	14.38 75	45.49 73	8 869 743	5.91 548	12.74 45	27.45 72	4.83 092
208	43 264	14.42 22	45.60 70	8 998 912	5.92 499	12.76 50	27.50 14	4.80 769
209	43 681	14.45 68	45.71 65	9 129 329	5.93 447	12.78 54	27.54 54	4.78 469
210	44 100	14.49 14	45.82 58	9 261 000	5.94 392	12.80 58	27.58 92	4.76 190
211	44 521	14.52 58	45.93 47	9 393 931	5.95 334	12.82 61	27.63 30	4.73 934
212	44 944	14.56 02	46.04 35	9 528 128	5.96 273	12.84 63	27.67 66	4.71 698
213	45 369	14.59 45	46.15 19	9 663 597	5.97 209	12.86 65	27.72 00	4.69 484
214	45 796	14.62 87	46.26 01	9 800 344	5.98 142	12.88 66	27.76 33	4.67 290
215	46 225	14.66 29	46.36 81	9 938 375	5.99 073	12.90 66	27.80 65	4.65 116
216	46 656	14.69 69	46.47 58	10 077 696	6.00 000	12.92 66	27.84 95	4.62 963
217	47 089	14.73 09	46.58 33	10 218 313	6.00 925	12.94 65	27.89 24	4.60 829
218	47 524	14.76 48	46.69 05	10 360 232	6.01 846	12.96 64	27.93 52	4.58 716
219	47 961	14.79 86	46.79 74	10 503 459	6.02 765	12.98 62	27.97 79	4.56 621
220	48 400	14.83 24	46.90 42	10 648 000	6.03 681	13.00 59	28.02 04	4.54 545
221	48 841	14.86 61	47.01 06	10 793 861	6.04 594	13.02 56	28.06 28	4.52 489
222	49 284	14.89 97	47.11 69	10 941 048	6.05 505	13.04 52	28.10 50	4.50 450
223	49 729	14.93 32	47.22 29	11 089 567	6.06 413	13.06 48	28.14 72	4.48 430
224	50 176	14.96 66	47.32 86	11 239 424	6.07 318	13.08 43	28.18 92	4.46 429
225	50 625	15.00 00	47.43 42	11 390 625	6.08 220	13.10 37	28.23 11	4.44 444
226	51 076	15.03 33	47.53 95	11 543 176	6.09 120	13.12 31	28.27 28	4.42 478
227	51 529	15.06 65	47.64 45	11 697 083	6.10 017	13.14 24	28.31 45	4.40 529
228	51 984	15.09 97	47.74 93	11 852 352	6.10 911	13.16 17	28.35 60	4.38 596
229	52 441	15.13 27	47.85 39	12 008 989	6.11 803	13.18 09	28.39 74	4.36 681
230	52 900	15.16 58	47.95 83	12 167 000	6.12 693	13.20 01	28.43 87	4.34 783
231	53 361	15.19 87	48.06 25	12 326 391	6.13 579	13.21 92	28.47 98	4.32 900
232	53 824	15.23 15	48.16 64	12 487 168	6.14 463	13.23 82	28.52 09	4.31 034
233	54 289	15.26 43	48.27 01	12 649 337	6.15 345	13.25 72	28.56 18	4.29 185
234	54 756	15.29 71	48.37 35	12 812 904	6.16 224	13.27 61	28.60 26	4.27 350
235	55 225	15.32 97	48.47 68	12 977 875	6.17 101	13.29 50	28.64 33	4.25 532
236	55 696	15.36 23	48.57 98	13 144 256	6.17 975	13.31 39	28.68 38	4.23 729
237	56 169	15.39 48	48.68 26	13 312 053	6.18 846	13.33 26	28.72 43	4.21 941
238	56 644	15.42 72	48.78 52	13 481 272	6.19 715	13.35 14	28.76 46	4.20 168
239	57 121	15.45 96	48.88 76	13 651 919	6.20 582	13.37 00	28.80 49	4.18 410
240	57 600	15.49 19	48.98 98	13 824 000	6.21 447	13.38 87	28.84 50	4.16 667
241	58 081	15.52 42	49.09 18	13 997 521	6.22 308	13.40 72	28.88 50	4.14 938
242	58 564	15.55 63	49.19 35	14 172 488	6.23 168	13.42 57	28.92 49	4.13 223
243	59 049	15.58 85	49.29 50	14 348 907	6.24 025	13.44 42	28.96 47	4.11 523
244	59 536	15.62 05	49.39 64	14 526 784	6.24 880	13.46 26	29.00 44	4.09 836
245	60 025	15.65 25	49.49 75	14 706 125	6.25 732	13.48 10	29.04 39	4.08 163
246	60 516	15.68 44	49.59 84	14 886 936	6.26 583	13.49 93	29.08 34	4.06 504
247	61 009	15.71 62	49.69 91	15 069 223	6.27 431	13.51 76	29.12 27	4.04 858
248	61 504	15.74 80	49.79 96	15 252 992	6.28 276	13.53 58	29.16 20	4.03 226
249	62 001	15.77 97	49.89 99	15 438 249	6.29 119	13.55 40	29.20 11	4.01 606
250	62 500	15.81 14	50.00 00	15 625 000	6.29 961	13.57 21	29.24 02	4.00 000
N	N^2	$\sqrt{N}$	$\sqrt{10N}$	N^3	$\sqrt[3]{N}$	$\sqrt[3]{10N}$	$\sqrt[3]{100N}$	$1000/N$

138

N	N^2	$\sqrt{N}$	$\sqrt{10N}$	N^3	$\sqrt[3]{N}$	$\sqrt[3]{10N}$	$\sqrt[3]{100N}$	1000 /N
250	62 500	15.81 14	50.00 00	15 625 000	6.29 961	13.57 21	29.24 02	4.00 000
251	63 001	15.84 30	50.09 99	15 813 251	6.30 799	13.59 02	29.27 91	3.98 406
252	63 504	15.87 45	50.19 96	16 003 008	6.31 636	13.60 82	29.31 79	3.96 825
253	64 009	15.90 60	50.29 91	16 194 277	6.32 470	13.62 62	29.35 67	3.95 257
254	64 516	15.93 74	50.39 84	16 387 064	6.33 303	13.64 41	29.39 53	3.93 701
255	65 025	15.96 87	50.49 75	16 581 375	6.34 133	13.66 20	29.43 38	3.92 157
256	65 536	16.00 00	50.59 64	16 777 216	6.34 960	13.67 98	29.47 23	3.90 625
257	66 049	16.03 12	50.69 52	16 974 593	6.35 786	13.69 76	29.51 06	3.89 105
258	66 564	16.06 24	50.79 37	17 173 512	6.36 610	13.71 53	29.54 88	3.87 597
259	67 081	16.09 35	50.89 20	17 373 979	6.37 431	13.73 30	29.58 69	3.86 100
260	67 600	16.12 45	50.99 02	17 576 000	6.38 250	13.75 07	29.62 50	3.84 615
261	68 121	16.15 55	51.08 82	17 779 581	6.39 068	13.76 83	29.66 29	3.83 142
262	68 644	16.18 64	51.18 59	17 984 728	6.39 883	13.78 59	29.70 07	3.81 679
263	69 169	16.21 73	51.28 35	18 191 447	6.40 696	13.80 34	29.73 85	3.80 228
264	69 696	16.24 81	51.38 09	18 399 744	6.41 507	13.82 08	29.77 61	3.78 788
265	70 225	16.27 88	51.47 82	18 609 625	6.42 316	13.83 83	29.81 37	3.77 358
266	70 756	16.30 95	51.57 52	18 821 096	6.43 123	13.85 57	29.85 11	3.75 940
267	71 289	16.34 01	51.67 20	19 034 163	6.43 928	13.87 30	29.88 85	3.74 532
268	71 824	16.37 07	51.76 87	19 248 832	6.44 731	13.89 03	29.92 57	3.73 134
269	72 361	16.40 12	51.86 52	19 465 109	6.45 531	13.90 76	29.96 29	3.71 747
270	72 900	16.43 17	51.96 15	19 683 000	6.46 330	13.92 48	30.00 00	3.70 370
271	73 441	16.46 21	52.05 77	19 902 511	6.47 127	13.94 19	30.03 70	3.69 004
272	73 984	16.49 24	52.15 36	20 123 648	6.47 922	13.95 91	30.07 39	3.67 647
273	74 529	16.52 27	52.24 94	20 346 417	6.48 715	13.97 61	30.11 07	3.66 300
274	75 076	16.55 29	52.34 50	20 570 824	6.49 507	13.99 32	30.14 74	3.64 964
275	75 625	16.58 31	52.44 04	20 796 875	6.50 296	14.01 02	30.18 41	3.63 636
276	76 176	16.61 32	52.53 57	21 024 576	6.51 083	14.02 72	30.22 06	3.62 319
277	76 729	16.64 33	52.63 08	21 253 933	6.51 868	14.04 41	30.25 70	3.61 011
278	77 284	16.67 33	52.72 57	21 484 952	6.52 652	14.06 10	30.29 34	3.59 712
279	77 841	16.70 33	52.82 05	21 717 639	6.53 434	14.07 78	30.32 97	3.58 423
280	78 400	16.73 32	52.91 50	21 952 000	6.54 213	14.09 46	30.36 59	3.57 143
281	78 961	16.76 31	53.00 94	22 188 041	6.54 991	14.11 14	30.40 20	3.55 872
282	79 524	16.79 29	53.10 37	22 425 768	6.55 767	14.12 81	30.43 80	3.54 610
283	80 089	16.82 26	53.19 77	22 665 187	6.56 541	14.14 48	30.47 40	3.53 357
284	80 656	16.85 23	53.29 17	22 906 304	6.57 314	14.16 14	30.50 98	3.52 113
285	81 225	16.88 19	53.38 54	23 149 125	6.58 084	14.17 80	30.54 56	3.50 877
286	81 796	16.91 15	53.47 90	23 393 656	6.58 853	14.19 46	30.58 13	3.49 650
287	82 369	16.94 11	53.57 24	23 639 903	6.59 620	14.21 11	30.61 69	3.48 432
288	82 944	16.97 06	53.66 56	23 887 872	6.60 385	14.22 76	30.65 24	3.47 222
289	83 521	17.00 00	53.75 87	24 137 569	6.61 149	14.24 40	30.68 78	3.46 021
290	84 100	17.02 94	53.85 16	24 389 000	6.61 911	14.26 04	30.72 32	3.44 828
291	84 681	17.05 87	53.94 44	24 642 171	6.62 671	14.27 68	30.75 84	3.43 643
292	85 264	17.08 80	54.03 70	24 897 088	6.63 429	14.29 31	30.79 36	3.42 466
293	85 849	17.11 72	54.12 95	25 153 757	6.64 185	14.30 94	30.82 87	3.41 297
294	86 436	17.14 64	54.22 18	25 412 184	6.64 940	14.32 57	30.86 38	3.40 136
295	87 025	17.17 56	54.31 39	25 672 375	6.65 693	14.34 19	30.89 87	3.38 983
296	87 616	17.20 47	54.40 59	25 934 336	6.66 444	14.35 81	30.93 36	3.37 838
297	88 209	17.23 37	54.49 77	26 198 073	6.67 194	14.37 43	30.96 84	3.36 700
298	88 804	17.26 27	54.58 94	26 463 592	6.67 942	14.39 04	31.00 31	3.35 570
299	89 401	17.29 16	54.68 09	26 730 899	6.68 688	14.40 65	31.03 78	3.34 448
300	90 000	17.32 05	54.77 23	27 000 000	6.69 433	14.42 25	31.07 23	3.33 333
N	N^2	$\sqrt{N}$	$\sqrt{10N}$	N^3	$\sqrt[3]{N}$	$\sqrt[3]{10N}$	$\sqrt[3]{100N}$	1000 /N

300 — Powers, Roots, Reciprocals — 350

N	N^2	$\sqrt{N}$	$\sqrt{10N}$	N^3	$\sqrt[3]{N}$	$\sqrt[3]{10N}$	$\sqrt[3]{100N}$	$1000/N$
300	90 000	17.32 05	54.77 23	27 000 000	6.69 433	14.42 25	31.07 23	3.33 333
301	90 601	17.34 94	54.86 35	27 270 901	6.70 176	14.43 85	31.10 68	3.32 226
302	91 204	17.37 81	54.95 45	27 543 608	6.70 917	14.45 45	31.14 12	3.31 126
303	91 809	17.40 69	55.04 54	27 818 127	6.71 657	14.47 04	31.17 56	3.30 033
304	92 416	17.43 56	55.13 62	28 094 464	6.72 395	14.48 63	31.20 98	3.28 947
305	93 025	17.46 42	55.22 68	28 372 625	6.73 132	14.50 22	31.24 40	3.27 869
306	93 636	17.49 29	55.31 73	28 652 616	6.73 866	14.51 80	31.27 81	3.26 797
307	94 249	17.52 14	55.40 76	28 934 443	6.74 600	14.53 38	31.31 21	3.25 733
308	94 864	17.54 99	55.49 77	29 218 112	6.75 331	14.54 96	31.34 61	3.24 675
309	95 481	17.57 84	55.58 78	29 503 629	6.76 061	14.56 53	31.38 00	3.23 625
310	96 100	17.60 68	55.67 76	29 791 000	6.76 790	14.58 10	31.41 38	3.22 581
311	96 721	17.63 52	55.76 74	30 080 231	6.77 517	14.59 67	31.44 75	3.21 543
312	97 344	17.66 35	55.85 70	30 371 328	6.78 242	14.61 23	31.48 12	3.20 513
313	97 969	17.69 18	55.94 64	30 664 297	6.78 966	14.62 79	31.51 48	3.19 489
314	98 596	17.72 00	56.03 57	30 959 144	6.79 688	14.64 34	31.54 83	3.18 471
315	99 225	17.74 82	56.12 49	31 255 875	6.80 409	14.65 90	31.58 18	3.17 460
316	99 856	17.77 64	56.21 39	31 554 496	6.81 128	14.67 45	31.61 52	3.16 456
317	100 489	17.80 45	56.30 28	31 855 013	6.81 846	14.68 99	31.64 85	3.15 457
318	101 124	17.83 26	56.39 15	32 157 432	6.82 562	14.70 54	31.68 17	3.14 465
319	101 761	17.86 06	56.48 01	32 461 759	6.83 277	14.72 08	31.71 49	3.13 480
320	102 400	17.88 85	56.56 85	32 768 000	6.83 990	14.73 61	31.74 80	3.12 500
321	103 041	17.91 65	56.65 69	33 076 161	6.84 702	14.75 15	31.78 11	3.11 526
322	103 684	17.94 44	56.74 50	33 386 248	6.85 412	14.76 68	31.81 40	3.10 559
323	104 329	17.97 22	56.83 31	33 698 267	6.86 121	14.78 20	31.84 69	3.09 598
324	104 976	18.00 00	56.92 10	34 012 224	6.86 829	14.79 73	31.87 98	3.08 642
325	105 625	18.02 78	57.00 88	34 328 125	6.87 534	14.81 25	31.91 25	3.07 692
326	106 276	18.05 55	57.09 64	34 645 976	6.88 239	14.82 77	31.94 52	3.06 748
327	106 929	18.08 31	57.18 39	34 965 783	6.88 942	14.84 28	31.97 78	3.05 810
328	107 584	18.11 08	57.27 13	35 287 552	6.89 643	14.85 79	32.01 04	3.04 878
329	108 241	18.13 84	57.35 85	35 611 289	6.90 344	14.87 30	32.04 29	3.03 951
330	108 900	18.16 59	57.44 56	35 937 000	6.91 042	14.88 81	32.07 53	3.03 030
331	109 561	18.19 34	57.53 26	36 264 691	6.91 740	14.90 31	32.10 77	3.02 115
332	110 224	18.22 09	57.61 94	36 594 368	6.92 436	14.91 81	32.14 00	3.01 205
333	110 889	18.24 83	57.70 62	36 926 037	6.93 130	14.93 30	32.17 22	3.00 300
334	111 556	18.27 57	57.79 27	37 259 704	6.93 823	14.94 80	32.20 44	2.99 401
335	112 225	18.30 30	57.87 92	37 595 375	6.94 515	14.96 29	32.23 65	2.98 507
336	112 896	18.33 03	57.96 55	37 933 056	6.95 205	14.97 77	32.26 86	2.97 619
337	113 569	18.35 76	58.05 17	38 272 753	6.95 894	14.99 26	32.30 06	2.96 736
338	114 244	18.38 48	58.13 78	38 614 472	6.96 582	15.00 74	32.33 25	2.95 858
339	114 921	18.41 20	58.22 37	38 958 219	6.97 268	15.02 22	32.36 43	2.94 985
340	115 600	18 43 91	58.30 95	39 304 000	6.97 953	15.03 69	32.39 61	2.94 118
341	116 281	18.46 62	58.39 52	39 651 821	6.98 637	15.05 17	32.42 78	2.93 255
342	116 964	18.49 32	58.48 08	40 001 688	6.99 319	15.06 64	32.45 95	2.92 398
343	117 649	18.52 03	58.56 62	40 353 607	7.00 000	15.08 10	32.49 11	2.91 545
344	118 336	18.54 72	58.65 15	40 707 584	7.00 680	15.09 57	32.52 27	2.90 698
345	119 025	18.57 42	58.73 67	41 063 625	7.01 358	15.11 03	32.55 42	2.89 855
346	119 716	18.60 11	58.82 18	41 421 736	7.02 035	15.12 49	32.58 56	2.89 017
347	120 409	18.62 79	58.90 67	41 781 923	7.02 711	15.13 94	32.61 69	2.88 184
348	121 104	18.65 48	58.99 15	42 144 192	7.03 385	15.15 40	32.64 82	2.87 356
349	121 801	18.68 15	59.07 62	42 508 549	7.04 058	15.16 85	32.67 95	2.86 533
350	122 500	18.70 83	59.16 08	42 875 000	7.04 730	15.18 29	32.71 07	2.85 714
N	N^2	$\sqrt{N}$	$\sqrt{10N}$	N^3	$\sqrt[3]{N}$	$\sqrt[3]{10N}$	$\sqrt[3]{100N}$	$1000/N$

140

350 — Powers, Roots, Reciprocals — 400

N	N²	√N	√10N	N³	∛N	∛10N	∛100N	1000/N
350	122 500	18.70 83	59.16 08	42 875 000	7.04 730	15.18 29	32.71 07	2.85 714
351	123 201	18.73 50	59.24 53	43 243 551	7.05 400	15.19 74	32.74 18	2.84 900
352	123 904	18.76 17	59.32 96	43 614 208	7.06 070	15.21 18	32.77 29	2.84 091
353	124 609	18.78 83	59.41 38	43 986 977	7.06 738	15.22 62	32.80 39	2.83 286
354	125 316	18.81 49	59.49 79	44 361 864	7.07 404	15.24 06	32.83 48	2.82 486
355	126 025	18.84 14	59.58 19	44 738 875	7.08 070	15.25 49	32.86 57	2.81 690
356	126 736	18.86 80	59.66 57	45 118 016	7.08 734	15.26 92	32.89 65	2.80 899
357	127 449	18.89 44	59.74 95	45 499 293	7.09 397	15.28 35	32.92 73	2.80 112
358	128 164	18.92 09	59.83 31	45 882 712	7.10 059	15.29 78	32.95 80	2.79 330
359	128 881	18.94 73	59.91 66	46 268 279	7.10 719	15.31 20	32.98 87	2.78 552
360	129 600	18.97 37	60.00 00	46 656 000	7.11 379	15.32 62	33.01 93	2.77 778
361	130 321	19.00 00	60.08 33	47 045 881	7.12 037	15.34 04	33.04 98	2.77 008
362	131 044	19.02 63	60.16 64	47 437 928	7.12 694	15.35 45	33.08 03	2.76 243
363	131 769	19.05 26	60.24 95	47 832 147	7.13 349	15.36 86	33.11 07	2.75 482
364	132 496	19.07 88	60.33 24	48 228 544	7.14 004	15.38 27	33.14 11	2.74 725
365	133 225	19.10 50	60.41 52	48 627 125	7.14 657	15.39 68	33.17 14	2.73 973
366	133 956	19.13 11	60.49 79	49 027 896	7.15 309	15.41 09	33.20 17	2.73 224
367	134 689	19.15 72	60.58 05	49 430 863	7.15 960	15.42 49	33.23 19	2.72 480
368	135 424	19.18 33	60.66 30	49 836 032	7.16 610	15.43 89	33.26 21	2.71 739
369	136 161	19.20 94	60.74 54	50 243 409	7.17 258	15.45 29	33.29 22	2.71 003
370	136 900	19.23 54	60.82 76	50 653 000	7.17 905	15.46 68	33.32 22	2.70 270
371	137 641	19.26 14	60.90 98	51 064 811	7.18 552	15.48 07	33.35 22	2.69 542
372	138 384	19.28 73	60.99 18	51 478 848	7.19 197	15.49 46	33.38 22	2.68 817
373	139 129	19.31 32	61.07 37	51 895 117	7.19 840	15.50 85	33.41 20	2.68 097
374	139 876	19.33 91	61.15 55	52 313 624	7.20 483	15.52 23	33.44 19	2.67 380
375	140 625	19.36 49	61.23 72	52 734 375	7.21 125	15.53 62	33.47 16	2.66 667
376	141 376	19.39 07	61.31 88	53 157 376	7.21 765	15.55 00	33.50 14	2.65 957
377	142 129	19.41 65	61.40 03	53 582 633	7.22 405	15.56 37	33.53 10	2.65 252
378	142 884	19.44 22	61.48 17	54 010 152	7.23 043	15.57 75	33.56 07	2.64 550
379	143 641	19.46 79	61.56 30	54 439 939	7.23 680	15.59 12	33.59 02	2.63 852
380	144 400	19.49 36	61.64 41	54 872 000	7.24 316	15.60 49	33.61 98	2.63 158
381	145 161	19.51 92	61.72 52	55 306 341	7.24 950	15.61 86	33.64 92	2.62 467
382	145 924	19.54 48	61.80 61	55 742 968	7.25 584	15.63 22	33.67 86	2.61 780
383	146 689	19.57 04	61.88 70	56 181 887	7.26 217	15.64 59	33.70 80	2.61 097
384	147 456	19.59 59	61.96 77	56 623 104	7.26 848	15.65 95	33.73 73	2.60 417
385	148 225	19.62 14	62.04 84	57 066 625	7.27 479	15.67 31	33.76 66	2.59 740
386	148 996	19.64 69	62.12 89	57 512 456	7.28 108	15.68 66	33.79 58	2.59 067
387	149 769	19.67 23	62.20 93	57 960 603	7.28 736	15.70 01	33.82 49	2.58 398
388	150 544	19.69 77	62.28 96	58 411 072	7.29 363	15.71 37	33.85 40	2.57 732
389	151 321	19.72 31	62.36 99	58 863 869	7.29 989	15.72 71	33.88 31	2.57 069
390	152 100	19.74 84	62.45 00	59 319 000	7.30 614	15.74 06	33.91 21	2.56 410
391	152 881	19.77 37	62.53 00	59 776 471	7.31 238	15.75 41	33.94 11	2.55 754
392	153 664	19.79 90	62.60 99	60 236 288	7.31 861	15.76 75	33.97 00	2.55 102
393	154 449	19.82 42	62.68 97	60 698 457	7.32 483	15.78 09	33.99 88	2.54 453
394	155 236	19.84 94	62.76 94	61 162 984	7.33 104	15.79 42	34.02 77	2.53 807
395	156 025	19.87 46	62.84 90	61 629 875	7.33 723	15.80 76	34.05 64	2.53 165
396	156 816	19.89 97	62.92 85	62 099 136	7.34 342	15.82 09	34.08 51	2.52 525
397	157 609	19.92 49	63.00 79	62 570 773	7.34 960	15.83 42	34.11 38	2.51 889
398	158 404	19.94 99	63.08 72	63 044 792	7.35 576	15.84 75	34.14 24	2.51 256
399	159 201	19.97 50	63.16 64	63 521 199	7.36 192	15.86 08	34.17 10	2.50 627
400	160 000	20.00 00	63.24 56	64 000 000	7.36 806	15.87 40	34.19 95	2.50 000
N	N²	√N	√10N	N³	∛N	∛10N	∛100N	1000/N

400 — Powers, Roots, Reciprocals — 450

N	N^2	$\sqrt{N}$	$\sqrt{10N}$	N^3	$\sqrt[3]{N}$	$\sqrt[3]{10N}$	$\sqrt[3]{100N}$	1000 /N
400	160 000	20.00 00	63.24 56	64 000 000	7.36 806	15.87 40	34.19 95	2.50 000
401	160 801	20.02 50	63.32 46	64 481 201	7.37 420	15.88 72	34.22 80	2.49 377
402	161 604	20.04 99	63.40 35	64 964 808	7.38 032	15.90 04	34.25 64	2.48 756
403	162 409	20.07 49	63.48 23	65 450 827	7.38 644	15.91 36	34.28 48	2.48 139
404	163 216	20.09 98	63.56 10	65 939 264	7.39 254	15.92 67	34.31 31	2.47 525
405	164 025	20.12 46	63.63 96	66 430 125	7.39 864	15.93 99	34.34 14	2.46 914
406	164 836	20.14 94	63.71 81	66 923 416	7.40 472	15.95 30	34.36 97	2.46 305
407	165 649	20.17 42	63.79 66	67 419 143	7.41 080	15.96 61	34.39 79	2.45 700
408	166 464	20.19 90	63.87 49	67 917 312	7.41 686	15.97 91	34.42 60	2.45 098
409	167 281	20.22 37	63.95 31	68 417 929	7.42 291	15.99 22	34.45 41	2.44 499
410	168 100	20.24 85	64.03 12	68 921 000	7.42 896	16.00 52	34.48 22	2.43 902
411	168 921	20.27 31	64.10 93	69 426 531	7.43 499	16.01 82	34.51 02	2.43 309
412	169 744	20.29 78	64.18 72	69 934 528	7.44 102	16.03 12	34.53 82	2.42 718
413	170 569	20.32 24	64.26 51	70 444 997	7.44 703	16.04 41	34.56 61	2.42 131
414	171 396	20.34 70	64.34 28	70 957 944	7.45 304	16.05 71	34.59 39	2.41 546
415	172 225	20.37 15	64.42 05	71 473 375	7.45 904	16.07 00	34.62 18	2.40 964
416	173 056	20.39 61	64.49 81	71 991 296	7.46 502	16.08 29	34.64 96	2.40 385
417	173 889	20.42 06	64.57 55	72 511 713	7.47 100	16.09 58	34.67 73	2.39 808
418	174 724	20.44 50	64.65 29	73 034 632	7.47 697	16.10 86	34.70 50	2.39 234
419	175 561	20.46 95	64.73 02	73 560 059	7.48 292	16.12 15	34.73 27	2.38 663
420	176 400	20.49 39	64.80 74	74 088 000	7.48 887	16.13 43	34.76 03	2.38 095
421	177 241	20.51 83	64.88 45	74 618 461	7.49 481	16.14 71	34.78 78	2.37 530
422	178 084	20.54 26	64.96 15	75 151 448	7.50 074	16.15 99	34.81 54	2.36 967
423	178 929	20.56 70	65.03 85	75 686 967	7.50 666	16.17 26	34.84 28	2.36 407
424	179 776	20.59 13	65.11 53	76 225 024	7.51 257	16.18 53	34.87 03	2.35 849
425	180 625	20.61 55	65.19 20	76 765 625	7.51 847	16.19 81	34.89 77	2.35 294
426	181 476	20.63 98	65.26 87	77 308 776	7.52 437	16.21 08	34.92 50	2.34 742
427	182 329	20.66 40	65.34 52	77 854 483	7.53 025	16.22 34	34.95 23	2.34 192
428	183 184	20.68 82	65.42 17	78 402 752	7.53 612	16.23 61	34.97 96	2.33 645
429	184 041	20.71 23	65.49 81	78 953 589	7.54 199	16.24 87	35.00 68	2.33 100
430	184 900	20.73 64	65.57 44	79 507 000	7.54 784	16.26 13	35.03 40	2.32 558
431	185 761	20.76 05	65.65 06	80 062 991	7.55 369	16.27 39	35.06 11	2.32 019
432	186 624	20.78 46	65.72 67	80 621 568	7.55 953	16.28 65	35.08 82	2.31 481
433	187 489	20.80 87	65.80 27	81 182 737	7.56 535	16.29 91	35.11 53	2.30 947
434	188 356	20.83 27	65.87 87	81 746 504	7.57 117	16.31 16	35.14 23	2.30 415
435	189 225	20.85 67	65.95 45	82 312 875	7.57 698	16.32 41	35.16 92	2.29 885
436	190 096	20.88 06	66.03 03	82 881 856	7.58 279	16.33 66	35.19 62	2.29 358
437	190 969	20.90 45	66.10 60	83 453 453	7.58 858	16.34 91	35.22 31	2.28 833
438	191 844	20.92 84	66.18 16	84 027 672	7.59 436	16.36 16	35.24 99	2.28 311
439	192 721	20.95 23	66.25 71	84 604 519	7.60 014	16.37 40	35.27 67	2.27 790
440	193 600	20.97 62	66.33 25	85 184 000	7.60 590	16.38 64	35.30 35	2.27 273
441	194 481	21.00 00	66.40 78	85 766 121	7.61 166	16.39 88	35.33 02	2.26 757
442	195 364	21.02 38	66.48 31	86 350 888	7.61 741	16.41 12	35.35 69	2.26 244
443	196 249	21.04 76	66.55 82	86 938 307	7.62 315	16.42 36	35.38 35	2.25 734
444	197 136	21.07 13	66.63 33	87 528 384	7.62 888	16.43 59	35.41 01	2.25 225
445	198 025	21.09 50	66.70 83	88 121 125	7.63 461	16.44 83	35.43 67	2.24 719
446	198 916	21.11 87	66.78 32	88 716 536	7.64 032	16.46 06	35.46 32	2.24 215
447	199 809	21.14 24	66.85 81	89 314 623	7.64 603	16.47 29	35.48 97	2.23 714
448	200 704	21.16 60	66.93 28	89 915 392	7.65 172	16.48 51	35.51 62	2.23 214
449	201 601	21.18 96	67.00 75	90 518 849	7.65 741	16.49 74	35.54 26	2.22 717
450	202 500	21.21 32	67.08 20	91 125 000	7.66 309	16.50 96	35.56 89	2.22 222
N	N^2	$\sqrt{N}$	$\sqrt{10N}$	N^3	$\sqrt[3]{N}$	$\sqrt[3]{10N}$	$\sqrt[3]{100N}$	1000 /N

450 — Powers, Roots, Reciprocals — 500

N	N²	√N	√10N	N³	∛N	∛10N	∛100N	1000/N
450	202 500	21.21 32	67.08 20	91 125 000	7.66 309	16.50 96	35.56 89	2.22 222
451	203 401	21.23 68	67.15 65	91 733 851	7.66 877	16.52 19	35.59 53	2.21 729
452	204 304	21.26 03	67.23 09	92 345 408	7.67 443	16.53 41	35.62 15	2.21 239
453	205 209	21.28 38	67.30 53	92 959 677	7.68 009	16.54 62	35.64 78	2.20 751
454	206 116	21.30 73	67.37 95	93 576 664	7.68 573	16.55 84	35.67 40	2.20 264
455	207 025	21.33 07	67.45 37	94 196 375	7.69 137	16.57 06	35.70 02	2.19 780
456	207 936	21.35 42	67.52 78	94 818 816	7.69 700	16.58 27	35.72 63	2.19 298
457	208 849	21.37 76	67.60 18	95 443 993	7.70 262	16.59 48	35.75 24	2.18 818
458	209 764	21.40 09	67.67 57	96 071 912	7.70 824	16.60 69	35.77 85	2.18 341
459	210 681	21.42 43	67.74 95	96 702 579	7.71 384	16.61 90	35.80 45	2.17 865
460	211 600	21.44 76	67.82 33	97 336 000	7.71 944	16.63 10	35.83 05	2.17 391
461	212 521	21.47 09	67.89 70	97 972 181	7.72 503	16.64 31	35.85 64	2.16 920
462	213 444	21.49 42	67.97 06	98 611 128	7.73 061	16.65 51	35.88 23	2.16 450
463	214 369	21.51 74	68.04 41	99 252 847	7.73 619	16.66 71	35.90 82	2.15 983
464	215 296	21.54 07	68.11 75	99 897 344	7.74 175	16.67 91	35.93 40	2.15 517
465	216 225	21.56 39	68.19 09	100 544 625	7.74 731	16.69 11	35.95 98	2.15 054
466	217 156	21.58 70	68.26 42	101 194 696	7.75 286	16.70 30	35.98 56	2.14 592
467	218 089	21.61 02	68.33 74	101 847 563	7.75 840	16.71 50	36.01 13	2.14 133
468	219 024	21.63 33	68.41 05	102 503 232	7.76 394	16.72 69	36.03 70	2.13 675
469	219 961	21.65 64	68.48 36	103 161 709	7.76 946	16.73 88	36.06 26	2.13 220
470	220 900	21.67 95	68.55 65	103 823 000	7.77 498	16.75 07	36.08 83	2.12 766
471	221 841	21.70 25	68.62 94	104 487 111	7.78 049	16.76 26	36.11 38	2.12 314
472	222 784	21.72 56	68.70 23	105 154 048	7.78 599	16.77 44	36.13 94	2.11 864
473	223 729	21.74 86	68.77 50	105 823 817	7.79 149	16.78 63	36.16 49	2.11 416
474	224 676	21.77 15	68.84 77	106 496 424	7.79 697	16.79 81	36.19 03	2.10 970
475	225 625	21.79 45	68.92 02	107 171 875	7.80 245	16.80 99	36.21 58	2.10 526
476	226 576	21.81 74	68.99 28	107 850 176	7.80 793	16.82 17	36.24 12	2.10 084
477	227 529	21.84 03	69.06 52	108 531 333	7.81 339	16.83 34	36.26 65	2.09 644
478	228 484	21.86 32	69.13 75	109 215 352	7.81 885	16.84 52	36.29 19	2.09 205
479	229 441	21.88 61	69.20 98	109 902 239	7.82 429	16.85 69	36.31 72	2.08 768
480	230 400	21.90 89	69.28 20	110 592 000	7.82 974	16.86 87	36.34 24	2.08 333
481	231 361	21.93 17	69.35 42	111 284 641	7.83 517	16.88 04	36.36 76	2.07 900
482	232 324	21.95 45	69.42 62	111 980 168	7.84 059	16.89 20	36.39 28	2.07 469
483	233 289	21.97 73	69.49 82	112 678 587	7.84 601	16.90 37	36.41 80	2.07 039
484	234 256	22.00 00	69.57 01	113 379 904	7.85 142	16.91 54	36.44 31	2.06 612
485	235 225	22.02 27	69.64 19	114 084 125	7.85 683	16.92 70	36.46 82	2.06 186
486	236 196	22.04 54	69.71 37	114 791 256	7.86 222	16.93 86	36.49 32	2.05 761
487	237 169	22.06 81	69.78 54	115 501 303	7.86 761	16.95 03	36.51 82	2.05 339
488	238 144	22.09 07	69.85 70	116 214 272	7.87 299	16.96 19	36.54 32	2.04 918
489	239 121	22.11 33	69.92 85	116 930 169	7.87 837	16.97 34	36.56 81	2.04 499
490	240 100	22.13 59	70.00 00	117 649 000	7.88 374	16.98 50	36.59 31	2.04 082
491	241 081	22.15 85	70.07 14	118 370 771	7.88 909	16.99 65	36.61 79	2.03 666
492	242 064	22.18 11	70.14 27	119 095 488	7.89 445	17.00 81	36.64 28	2.03 252
493	243 049	22.20 36	70.21 40	119 823 157	7.89 979	17.01 96	36.66 76	2.02 840
494	244 036	22.22 61	70.28 51	120 553 784	7.90 513	17.03 11	36.69 24	2.02 429
495	245 025	22.24 86	70.35 62	121 287 375	7.91 046	17.04 26	36.71 71	2.02 020
496	246 016	22.27 11	70.42 73	122 023 936	7.91 578	17.05 40	36.74 18	2.01 613
497	247 009	22.29 35	70.49 82	122 763 473	7.92 110	17.06 55	36.76 65	2.01 207
498	248 004	22.31 59	70.56 91	123 505 992	7.92 641	17.07 69	36.79 11	2.00 803
499	249 001	22.33 83	70.63 99	124 251 499	7.93 171	17.08 84	36.81 57	2.00 401
500	250 000	22.36 07	70.71 07	125 000 000	7.93 701	17.09 98	36.84 03	2.00 000
N	N²	√N	√10N	N³	∛N	∛10N	∛100N	1000/N

500 — Powers, Roots, Reciprocals — 550

N	N²	√N	√10N	N³	∛N	∛10N	∛100N	1000 /N
500	250 000	22.36 07	70.71 07	125 000 000	7.93 701	17.09 98	36.84 03	2.00 000
501	251 001	22.38 30	70.78 14	125 751 501	7.94 229	17.11 12	36.86 49	1.99 601
502	252 004	22.40 54	70.85 20	126 506 008	7.94 757	17.12 25	36.88 94	1.99 203
503	253 009	22.42 77	70.92 25	127 263 527	7.95 285	17.13 39	36.91 38	1.98 807
504	254 016	22.44 99	70.99 30	128 024 064	7.95 811	17.14 52	36.93 83	1.98 413
505	255 025	22.47 22	71.06 34	128 787 625	7.96 337	17.15 66	36.96 27	1.98 020
506	256 036	22.49 44	71.13 37	129 554 216	7.96 863	17.16 79	36.98 71	1.97 628
507	257 049	22.51 67	71.20 39	130 323 843	7.97 387	17.17 92	37.01 14	1.97 239
508	258 064	22.53 89	71.27 41	131 096 512	7.97 911	17.19 05	37.03 58	1.96 850
509	259 081	22.56 10	71.34 42	131 872 229	7.98 434	17.20 17	37.06 00	1.96 464
510	260 100	22.58 32	71.41 43	132 651 000	7.98 957	17.21 30	37.08 43	1.96 078
511	261 121	22.60 53	71.48 43	133 432 831	7.99 479	17.22 42	37.10 85	1.95 695
512	262 144	22.62 74	71.55 42	134 217 728	8.00 000	17.23 55	37.13 27	1.95 312
513	263 169	22.64 95	71.62 40	135 005 697	8.00 520	17.24 67	37.15 69	1.94 932
514	264 196	22.67 16	71.69 38	135 796 744	8.01 040	17.25 79	37.18 10	1.94 553
515	265 225	22.69 36	71.76 35	136 590 875	8.01 559	17.26 91	37.20 51	1.94 175
516	266 256	22.71 56	71.83 31	137 388 096	8.02 078	17.28 02	37.22 92	1.93 798
517	267 289	22.73 76	71.90 27	138 188 413	8.02 596	17.29 14	37.25 32	1.93 424
518	268 324	22.75 96	71.97 22	138 991 832	8.03 113	17.30 25	37.27 72	1.93 050
519	269 361	22.78 16	72.04 17	139 798 359	8.03 629	17.31 37	37.30 12	1.92 678
520	270 400	22.80 35	72.11 10	140 608 000	8.04 145	17.32 48	37.32 51	1.92 308
521	271 441	22.82 54	72.18 03	141 420 761	8.04 660	17.33 59	37.34 90	1.91 939
522	272 484	22.84 73	72.24 96	142 236 648	8.05 175	17.34 70	37.37 29	1.91 571
523	273 529	22.86 92	72.31 87	143 055 667	8.05 689	17.35 80	37.39 68	1.91 205
524	274 576	22.89 10	72.38 78	143 877 824	8.06 202	17.36 91	37.42 06	1.90 840
525	275 625	22.91 29	72.45 69	144 703 125	8.06 714	17.38 01	37.44 44	1.90 476
526	276 676	22.93 47	72.52 59	145 531 576	8.07 226	17.39 12	37.46 81	1.90 114
527	277 729	22.95 65	72.59 48	146 363 183	8.07 737	17.40 22	37.49 18	1.89 753
528	278 784	22.97 83	72.66 36	147 197 952	8.08 248	17.41 32	37.51 55	1.89 394
529	279 841	23.00 00	72.73 24	148 035 889	8.08 758	17.42 42	37.53 92	1.89 036
530	280 900	23.02 17	72.80 11	148 877 000	8.09 267	17.43 51	37.56 29	1.88 679
531	281 961	23.04 34	72.86 97	149 721 291	8.09 776	17.44 61	37.58 65	1.88 324
532	283 024	23.06 51	72.93 83	150 568 768	8.10 284	17.45 70	37.61 01	1.87 970
533	284 089	23.08 68	73.00 68	151 419 437	8.10 791	17.46 80	37.63 36	1.87 617
534	285 156	23.10 84	73.07 53	152 273 304	8.11 298	17.47 89	37.65 71	1.87 266
535	286 225	23.13 01	73.14 37	153 130 375	8.11 804	17.48 98	37.68 06	1.86 916
536	287 296	23.15 17	73.21 20	153 990 656	8.12 310	17.50 07	37.70 41	1.86 567
537	288 369	23.17 33	73.28 03	154 854 153	8.12 814	17.51 16	37.72 75	1.86 220
538	289 444	23.19 48	73.34 85	155 720 872	8.13 319	17.52 24	37.75 09	1.85 874
539	290 521	23.21 64	73.41 66	156 590 819	8.13 822	17.53 33	37.77 43	1.85 529
540	291 600	23.23 79	73.48 47	157 464 000	8.14 325	17.54 41	37.79 76	1.85 185
541	292 681	23.25 94	73.55 27	158 340 421	8.14 828	17.55 49	37.82 09	1.84 843
542	293 764	23.28 09	73.62 06	159 220 088	8.15 329	17.56 57	37.84 42	1.84 502
543	294 849	23.30 24	73.68 85	160 103 007	8.15 831	17.57 65	37.86 75	1.84 162
544	295 936	23.32 38	73.75 64	160 989 184	8.16 331	17.58 73	37.89 07	1.83 824
545	297 025	23.34 52	73.82 41	161 878 625	8.16 831	17.59 81	37.91 39	1.83 486
546	298 116	23.36 66	73.89 18	162 771 336	8.17 330	17.60 88	37.93 71	1.83 150
547	299 209	23.38 80	73.95 94	163 667 323	8.17 829	17.61 96	37.96 03	1.82 815
548	300 304	23.40 94	74.02 70	164 566 592	8.18 327	17.63 03	37.98 34	1.82 482
549	301 401	23.43 07	74.09 45	165 469 149	8.18 824	17.64 10	38.00 65	1.82 149
550	302 500	23.45 21	74.16 20	166 375 000	8.19 321	17.65 17	38.02 95	1.81 818
N	N²	√N	√10N	N³	∛N	∛10N	∛100N	1000 /N

550 — Powers, Roots, Reciprocals — 600

N	N²	√N	√10N	N³	∛N	∛10N	∛100N	1000/N
550	302 500	23.45 21	74.16 20	166 375 000	8.19 321	17.65 17	38.02 95	1.81 818
551	303 601	23.47 34	74.22 94	167 284 151	8.19 818	17.66 24	38.05 26	1.81 488
552	304 704	23.49 47	74.29 67	168 196 608	8.20 313	17.67 31	38.07 56	1.81 159
553	305 809	23.51 60	74.36 40	169 112 377	8.20 808	17.68 38	38.09 85	1.80 832
554	306 916	23.53 72	74.43 12	170 031 464	8.21 303	17.69 44	38.12 15	1.80 505
555	308 025	23.55 84	74.49 83	170 953 875	8.21 797	17.70 51	38.14 44	1.80 180
556	309 136	23.57 97	74.56 54	171 879 616	8.22 290	17.71 57	38.16 73	1.79 856
557	310 249	23.60 08	74.63 24	172 808 693	8.22 783	17.72 63	38.19 02	1.79 553
558	311 364	23.62 20	74.69 94	173 741 112	8.23 275	17.73 69	38.21 30	1.79 211
559	312 481	23.64 32	74.76 63	174 676 879	8.23 766	17.74 75	38.23 58	1.78 891
560	313 600	23.66 43	74.83 31	175 616 000	8.24 257	17.75 81	38.25 86	1.78 571
561	314 721	23.68 54	74.89 99	176 558 481	8.24 747	17.76 86	38.28 14	1.78 253
562	315 844	23.70 65	74.96 67	177 504 328	8.25 237	17.77 92	38.30 41	1.77 936
563	316 969	23.72 76	75.03 33	178 453 547	8.25 726	17.78 97	38.32 68	1.77 620
564	318 096	23.74 87	75.09 99	179 406 144	8.26 215	17.80 03	38.34 95	1.77 305
565	319 225	23.76 97	75.16 65	180 362 125	8.26 703	17.81 08	38.37 22	1.76 991
566	320 356	23.79 08	75.23 30	181 321 496	8.27 190	17.82 13	38.39 48	1.76 678
567	321 489	23.81 18	75.29 94	182 284 263	8.27 677	17.83 18	38.41 74	1.76 367
568	322 624	23.83 28	75.36 58	183 250 432	8.28 164	17.84 22	38.43 99	1.76 056
569	323 761	23.85 37	75.43 21	184 220 009	8.28 649	17.85 27	38.46 25	1.75 747
570	324 900	23.87 47	75.49 83	185 193 000	8.29 134	17.86 32	38.48 50	1.75 439
571	326 041	23.89 56	75.56 45	186 169 411	8.29 619	17.87 36	38.50 75	1.75 131
572	327 184	23.91 65	75.63 07	187 149 248	8.30 103	17.88 40	38.53 00	1.74 825
573	328 329	23.93 74	75.69 68	188 132 517	8.30 587	17.89 44	38.55 24	1.74 520
574	329 476	23.95 83	75.76 28	189 119 224	8.31 069	17.90 48	38.57 48	1.74 216
575	330 625	23.97 92	75.82 88	190 109 375	8.31 552	17.91 52	38.59 72	1.73 913
576	331 776	24.00 00	75.89 47	191 102 976	8.32 034	17.92 56	38.61 96	1.73 611
577	332 929	24.02 08	75.96 05	192 100 033	8.32 515	17.93 60	38.64 19	1.73 310
578	334 084	24.04 16	76.02 63	193 100 552	8.32 995	17.94 63	38.66 42	1.73 010
579	335 241	24.06 24	76.09 20	194 104 539	8.33 476	17.95 67	38.68 65	1.72 712
580	336 400	24.08 32	76.15 77	195 112 000	8.33 955	17.96 70	38.70 88	1.72 414
581	337 561	24.10 39	76.22 34	196 122 941	8.34 434	17.97 73	38.73 10	1.72 117
582	338 724	24.12 47	76.28 89	197 137 368	8.34 913	17.98 76	38.75 32	1.71 821
583	339 889	24.14 54	76.35 44	198 155 287	8.35 390	17.99 79	38.77 54	1.71 527
584	341 056	24.16 61	76.41 99	199 176 704	8.35 868	18.00 82	38.79 75	1.71 233
585	342 225	24.18 68	76.48 53	200 201 625	8.36 345	18.01 85	38.81 97	1.70 940
586	343 396	24.20 74	76.55 06	201 230 056	8.36 821	18.02 88	38.84 18	1.70 648
587	344 569	24.22 81	76.61 59	202 262 003	8.37 297	18.03 90	38.86 39	1.70 358
588	345 744	24.24 87	76.68 12	203 297 472	8.37 772	18.04 92	38.88 59	1.70 068
589	346 921	24.26 93	76.74 63	204 336 469	8.38 247	18.05 95	38.90 80	1.69 779
590	348 100	24.28 99	76.81 15	205 379 000	8.38 721	18.06 97	38.93 00	1.69 492
591	349 281	24.31 05	76.87 65	206 425 071	8.39 194	18.07 99	38.95 19	1.69 205
592	350 464	24.33 11	76.94 15	207 474 688	8.39 667	18.09 01	38.97 39	1.68 919
593	351 649	24.35 16	77.00 65	208 527 857	8.40 140	18.10 03	38.99 58	1.68 634
594	352 836	24.37 21	77.07 14	209 584 584	8.40 612	18.11 04	39.01 77	1.68 350
595	354 025	24.39 26	77.13 62	210 644 875	8.41 083	18.12 06	39.03 96	1.68 067
596	355 216	24.41 31	77.20 10	211 708 736	8.41 554	18.13 07	39.06 15	1.67 785
597	356 409	24.43 36	77.26 58	212 776 173	8.42 025	18.14 09	39.08 33	1.67 504
598	357 604	24.45 40	77.33 05	213 847 192	8.42 494	18.15 10	39.10 51	1.67 224
599	358 801	24.47 45	77.39 51	214 921 799	8.42 964	18.16 11	39.12 69	1.66 945
600	360 000	24.49 49	77.45 97	216 000 000	8.43 433	18.17 12	39.14 87	1.66 667
N	N²	√N	√10N	N³	∛N	∛10N	∛100N	1000/N

600 — Powers, Roots, Reciprocals — 650

N	N^2	$\sqrt{N}$	$\sqrt{10N}$	N^3	$\sqrt[3]{N}$	$\sqrt[3]{10N}$	$\sqrt[3]{100N}$	1000/N
600	360 000	24.49 49	77.45 97	216 000 000	8.43 433	18.17 12	39.14 87	1.66 667
601	361 201	24.51 53	77.52 42	217 081 801	8.43 901	18.18 13	39.17 04	1.66 389
602	362 404	24.53 57	77.58 87	218 167 208	8.44 369	18.19 14	39.19 21	1.66 113
603	363 609	24.55 61	77.65 31	219 256 227	8.44 836	18.20 14	39.21 38	1.65 837
604	364 816	24.57 64	77.71 74	220 348 864	8.45 303	18.21 15	39.23 55	1.65 563
605	366 025	24.59 67	77.78 17	221 445 125	8.45 769	18.22 15	39.25 71	1.65 289
606	367 236	24.61 71	77.84 60	222 545 016	8.46 235	18.23 16	39.27 87	1.65 017
607	368 449	24.63 74	77.91 02	223 648 543	8.46 700	18.24 16	39.30 03	1.64 745
608	369 664	24.65 77	77.97 44	224 755 712	8.47 165	18.25 16	39.32 19	1.64 474
609	370 881	24.67 79	78.03 85	225 866 529	8.47 629	18.26 16	39.34 34	1.64 204
610	372 100	24.69 82	78.10 25	226 981 000	8.48 093	18.27 16	39.36 50	1.63 934
611	373 321	24.71 84	78.16 65	228 099 131	8.48 556	18.28 16	39.38 65	1.63 666
612	374 544	24.73 86	78.23 04	229 220 928	8.49 018	18.29 15	39.40 79	1.63 399
613	375 769	24.75 88	78.29 43	230 346 397	8.49 481	18.30 15	39.42 94	1.63 132
614	376 996	24.77 90	78.35 82	231 475 544	8.49 942	18.31 15	39.45 08	1.62 866
615	378 225	24.79 92	78.42 19	232 608 375	8.50 404	18.32 14	39.47 22	1.62 602
616	379 456	24.81 93	78.48 57	233 744 896	8.50 864	18.33 13	39.49 36	1.62 338
617	380 689	24.83 95	78.54 93	234 885 113	8.51 324	18.34 12	39.51 50	1.62 075
618	381 924	24.85 96	78.61 30	236 029 032	8.51 784	18.35 11	39.53 63	1.61 812
619	383 161	24.87 97	78.67 66	237 176 659	8.52 243	18.36 10	39.55 76	1.61 551
620	384 400	24.89 98	78.74 01	238 328 000	8.52 702	18.37 09	39.57 89	1.61 290
621	385 641	24.91 99	78.80 36	239 483 061	8.53 160	18.38 08	39.60 02	1.61 031
622	386 884	24.93 99	78.86 70	240 641 848	8.53 618	18.39 06	39.62 14	1.60 772
623	388 129	24.96 00	78.93 03	241 804 367	8.54 075	18.40 05	39.64 27	1.60 514
624	389 376	24.98 00	78.99 37	242 970 624	8.54 532	18.41 03	39.66 38	1.60 256
625	390 625	25.00 00	79.05 69	244 140 625	8.54 988	18.42 02	39.68 50	1.60 000
626	391 876	25.02 00	79.12 02	245 314 376	8.55 444	18.43 00	39.70 62	1.59 744
627	393 129	25.04 00	79.18 33	246 491 883	8.55 899	18.43 98	39.72 73	1.59 490
628	394 384	25.05 99	79.24 65	247 673 152	8.56 354	18.44 96	39.74 84	1.59 236
629	395 641	25.07 99	79.30 95	248 858 189	8.56 808	18.45 94	39.76 95	1.58 983
630	396 900	25.09 98	79.37 25	250 047 000	8.57 262	18.46 91	39.79 06	1.58 730
631	398 161	25.11 97	79.43 55	251 239 591	8.57 715	18.47 89	39.81 16	1.58 479
632	399 424	25.13 96	79.49 84	252 435 968	8.58 168	18.48 87	39.83 26	1.58 228
633	400 689	25.15 95	79.56 13	253 636 137	8.58 620	18.49 84	39.85 36	1.57 978
634	401 956	25.17 94	79.62 41	254 840 104	8.59 072	18.50 82	39.87 46	1.57 729
635	403 225	25.19 92	79.68 69	256 047 875	8.59 524	18.51 79	39.89 56	1.57 480
636	404 496	25.21 90	79.74 96	257 259 456	8.59 975	18.52 76	39.91 65	1.57 233
637	405 769	25.23 89	79.81 23	258 474 853	8.60 425	18.53 73	39.93 74	1.56 986
638	407 044	25.25 87	79.87 49	259 694 072	8.60 875	18.54 70	39.95 83	1.56 740
639	408 321	25.27 84	79.93 75	260 917 119	8.61 325	18.55 67	39.97 92	1.56 495
640	409 600	25.29 82	80.00 00	262 144 000	8.61 774	18.56 64	40.00 00	1.56 250
641	410 881	25.31 80	80.06 25	263 374 721	8.62 222	18.57 60	40.02 08	1.56 006
642	412 164	25.33 77	80.12 49	264 609 288	8.62 671	18.58 57	40.04 16	1.55 763
643	413 449	25.35 74	80.18 73	265 847 707	8.63 118	18.59 53	40.06 24	1.55 521
644	414 736	25.37 72	80.24 96	267 089 984	8.63 566	18.60 50	40.08 32	1.55 280
645	416 025	25.39 69	80.31 19	268 336 125	8.64 012	18.61 46	40.10 39	1.55 039
646	417 316	25.41 65	80.37 41	269 586 136	8.64 459	18.62 42	40.12 46	1.54 799
647	418 609	25.43 62	80.43 63	270 840 023	8.64 904	18.63 38	40.14 53	1.54 560
648	419 904	25.45 58	80.49 84	272 097 792	8.65 350	18.64 34	40.16 60	1.54 321
649	421 201	25.47 55	80.56 05	273 359 449	8.65 795	18.65 30	40.18 66	1.54 083
650	422 500	25.49 51	80.62 26	274 625 000	8.66 239	18.66 26	40.20 73	1.53 846
N	N^2	$\sqrt{N}$	$\sqrt{10N}$	N^3	$\sqrt[3]{N}$	$\sqrt[3]{10N}$	$\sqrt[3]{100N}$	1000/N

146

N	N^2	$\sqrt{N}$	$\sqrt{10N}$	N^3	$\sqrt[3]{N}$	$\sqrt[3]{10N}$	$\sqrt[3]{100N}$	1000 /N
650	422 500	25.49 51	80.62 26	274 625 000	8.66 239	18.66 26	40.20 73	1.53 846
651	423 801	25.51 47	80.68 46	275 894 451	8.66 683	18.67 21	40.22 79	1.53 610
652	425 104	25.53 43	80.74 65	277 167 808	8.67 127	18.68 17	40.24 85	1.53 374
653	426 409	25.55 39	80.80 84	278 445 077	8.67 570	18.69 12	40.26 90	1.53 139
654	427 716	25.57 34	80.87 03	279 726 264	8.68 012	18.70 08	40.28 96	1.52 905
655	429 025	25.59 30	80.93 21	281 011 375	8.68 455	18.71 03	40.31 01	1.52 672
656	430 336	25.61 25	80.99 38	282 300 416	8.68 896	18.71 98	40.33 06	1.52 439
657	431 649	25.63 20	81.05 55	283 593 393	8.69 338	18.72 93	40.35 11	1.52 207
658	432 964	25.65 15	81.11 72	284 890 312	8.69 778	18.73 88	40.37 15	1.51 976
659	434 281	25.67 10	81.17 88	286 191 179	8.70 219	18.74 83	40.39 20	1.51 745
660	435 600	25.69 05	81.24 04	287 496 000	8.70 659	18.75 78	40.41 24	1.51 515
661	436 921	25.70 99	81.30 19	288 804 781	8.71 098	18.76 72	40.43 28	1.51 286
662	438 244	25.72 94	81.36 34	290 117 528	8.71 537	18.77 67	40.45 32	1.51 057
663	439 569	25.74 88	81.42 48	291 434 247	8.71 976	18.78 62	40.47 35	1.50 830
664	440 896	25.76 82	81.48 62	292 754 944	8.72 414	18.79 56	40.49 39	1.50 602
665	442 225	25.78 76	81.54 75	294 079 625	8.72 852	18.80 50	40.51 42	1.50 376
666	443 556	25.80 70	81.60 88	295 408 296	8.73 289	18.81 44	40.53 45	1.50 150
667	444 889	25.82 63	81.67 01	296 740 963	8.73 726	18.82 39	40.55 48	1.49 925
668	446 224	25.84 57	81.73 13	298 077 632	8.74 162	18.83 33	40.57 50	1.49 701
669	447 561	25.86 50	81.79 24	299 418 309	8.74 598	18.84 27	40.59 53	1.49 477
670	448 900	25.88 44	81.85 35	300 763 000	8.75 034	18.85 20	40.61 55	1.49 254
671	450 241	25.90 37	81.91 46	302 111 711	8.75 469	18.86 14	40.63 57	1.49 031
672	451 584	25.92 30	81.97 56	303 464 448	8.75 904	18.87 08	40.65 59	1.48 810
673	452 929	25.94 22	82.03 66	304 821 217	8.76 338	18.88 01	40.67 60	1.48 588
674	454 276	25.96 15	82.09 75	306 182 024	8.76 772	18.88 95	40.69 61	1.48 368
675	455 625	25.98 08	82.15 84	307 546 875	8.77 205	18.89 88	40 71 63	1.48 148
676	456 976	26.00 00	82.21 92	308 915 776	8.77 638	18.90 81	40.73 64	1.47 929
677	458 329	26.01 92	82.28 00	310 288 733	8.78 071	18.91 75	40.75 64	1.47 710
678	459 684	26.03 84	82.34 08	311 665 752	8.78 503	18.92 68	40.77 65	1.47 493
679	461 041	26.05 76	82.40 15	313 046 839	8.78 935	18.93 61	40.79 65	1.47 275
680	462 400	26.07 68	82.46 21	314 432 000	8.79 366	18.94 54	40.81 66	1.47 059
681	463 761	26.09 60	82.52 27	315 821 241	8.79 797	18.95 46	40.83 65	1.46 843
682	465 124	26.11 51	82.58 33	317 214 568	8.80 227	18.96 39	40.85 65	1.46 628
683	466 489	26.13 43	82.64 38	318 611 987	8.80 657	18.97 32	40.87 65	1.46 413
684	467 856	26.15 34	82.70 43	320 013 504	8.81 087	18.98 24	40.89 64	1.46 199
685	469 225	26.17 25	82.76 47	321 419 125	8.81 516	18.99 17	40.91 63	1.45 985
686	470 596	26.19 16	82.82 51	322 828 856	8.81 945	19.00 09	40.93 62	1.45 773
687	471 969	26.21 07	82.88 55	324 242 703	8.82 373	19.01 02	40.95 61	1.45 560
688	473 344	26.22 98	82.94 58	325 660 672	8.82 801	19.01 94	40.97 60	1.45 349
689	474 721	26.24 88	83.00 60	327 082 769	8.83 228	19.02 86	40.99 58	1.45 138
690	476 100	26.26 79	83.06 62	328 509 000	8.83 656	19.03 78	41.01 57	1.44 928
691	477 481	26.28 69	83.12 64	329 939 371	8.84 082	19.04 70	41.03 55	1.44 718
692	478 864	26.30 59	83.18 65	331 373 888	8.84 509	19.05 62	41.05 52	1.44 509
693	480 249	26.32 49	83.24 66	332 812 557	8.84 934	19.06 53	41.07 50	1.44 300
694	481 636	26.34 39	83.30 67	334 255 384	8.85 360	19.07 45	41.09 48	1.44 092
695	483 025	26.36 29	83.36 67	335 702 375	8.85 785	19.08 37	41.11 45	1.43 885
696	484 416	26.38 18	83.42 66	337 153 536	8.86 210	19.09 28	41.13 42	1.43 678
697	485 809	26.40 08	83.48 65	338 608 873	8.86 634	19.10 19	41.15 39	1.43 472
698	487 204	26.41 97	83.54 64	340 068 392	8.87 058	19.11 11	41.17 36	1.43 266
699	488 601	26.43 86	83.60 62	341 532 099	8.87 481	19.12 02	41.19 32	1.43 062
700	490 000	26.45 75	83.66 60	343 000 000	8.87 904	19.12 93	41.21 29	1.42 857
N	N^2	$\sqrt{N}$	$\sqrt{10N}$	N^3	$\sqrt[3]{N}$	$\sqrt[3]{10N}$	$\sqrt[3]{100N}$	1000 /N

700 — Powers, Roots, Reciprocals — 750

N	N²	√N	√10N	N³	∛N	∛10N	∛100N	1000 /N
700	490 000	26.45 75	83.66 60	343 000 000	8.87 904	19.12 93	41.21 29	1.42 857
701	491 401	26.47 64	83.72 57	344 472 101	8.88 327	19.13 84	41.23 25	1.42 653
702	492 804	26.49 53	83.78 54	345 948 408	8.88 749	19.14 75	41.25 21	1.42 450
703	494 209	26.51 41	83.84 51	347 428 927	8.89 171	19.15 66	41.27 16	1.42 248
704	495 616	26.53 30	83.90 47	348 913 664	8.89 592	19.16 57	41.29 12	1.42 045
705	497 025	26.55 18	83.96 43	350 402 625	8.90 013	19.17 47	41.31 07	1.41 844
706	498 436	26.57 07	84.02 38	351 895 816	8.90 434	19.18 38	41.33 03	1.41 643
707	499 849	26.58 95	84.08 33	353 393 243	8.90 854	19.19 29	41.34 98	1.41 443
708	501 264	26.60 83	84.14 27	354 894 912	8.91 274	19.20 19	41.36 93	1.41 243
709	502 681	26.62 71	84.20 21	356 400 829	8.91 693	19.21 09	41.38 87	1.41 044
710	504 100	26.64 58	84.26 15	357 911 000	8.92 112	19.22 00	41.40 82	1.40 845
711	505 521	26.66 46	84.32 08	359 425 431	8.92 531	19.22 90	41.42 76	1.40 647
712	506 944	26.68 33	84.38 01	360 944 128	8.92 949	19.23 80	41.44 70	1.40 449
713	508 369	26.70 21	84.43 93	362 467 097	8.93 367	19.24 70	41.46 64	1.40 252
714	509 796	26.72 08	84.49 85	363 994 344	8.93 784	19.25 60	41.48 58	1.40 056
715	511 225	26.73 95	84.55 77	365 525 875	8.94 201	19.26 50	41.50 52	1.39 860
716	512 656	26.75 82	84.61 68	367 061 696	8.94 618	19.27 40	41.52 45	1.39 665
717	514 089	26.77 69	84.67 59	368 601 813	8.95 034	19.28 29	41.54 38	1.39 470
718	515 524	26.79 55	84.73 49	370 146 232	8.95 450	19.29 19	41.56 31	1.39 276
719	516 961	26.81 42	84.79 39	371 694 959	8.95 866	19.30 08	41.58 24	1.39 082
720	518 400	26.83 28	84.85 28	373 248 000	8.96 281	19.30 98	41.60 17	1.38 889
721	519 841	26.85 14	84.91 17	374 805 361	8.96 696	19.31 87	41.62 09	1.38 696
722	521 284	26.87 01	84.97 06	376 367 048	8.97 110	19.32 77	41.64 02	1.38 504
723	522 729	26.88 87	85.02 94	377 933 067	8.97 524	19.33 66	41.65 94	1.38 313
724	524 176	26.90 72	85.08 82	379 503 424	8.97 938	19.34 55	41.67 86	1.38 122
725	525 625	26.92 58	85.14 69	381 078 125	8.98 351	19.35 44	41.69 78	1.37 931
726	527 076	26.94 44	85.20 56	382 657 176	8.98 764	19.36 33	41.71 69	1.37 741
727	528 529	26.96 29	85.26 43	384 240 583	8.99 176	19.37 22	41.73 61	1.37 552
728	529 984	26.98 15	85.32 29	385 828 352	8.99 588	19.38 10	41.75 52	1.37 363
729	531 441	27.00 00	85.38 15	387 420 489	9.00 000	19.38 99	41.77 43	1.37 174
730	532 900	27.01 85	85.44 00	389 017 000	9.00 411	19.39 88	41.79 34	1.36 986
731	534 361	27.03 70	85.49 85	390 617 891	9.00 822	19.40 76	41.81 25	1.36 799
732	535 824	27.05 55	85.55 70	392 223 168	9.01 233	19.41 65	41.83 15	1.36 612
733	537 289	27.07 40	85.61 54	393 832 837	9.01 643	19.42 53	41.85 06	1.36 426
734	538 756	27.09 24	85.67 38	395 446 904	9.02 053	19.43 41	41.86 96	1.36 240
735	540 225	27.11 09	85.73 21	397 065 375	9.02 462	19.44 30	41.88 86	1.36 054
736	541 696	27.12 93	85.79 04	398 688 256	9.02 871	19.45 18	41.90 76	1.35 870
737	543 169	27.14 77	85.84 87	400 315 553	9.03 280	19.46 06	41.92 66	1.35 685
738	544 644	27.16 62	85.90 69	401 947 272	9.03 689	19.46 94	41.94 55	1.35 501
739	546 121	27.18 46	85.96 51	403 583 419	9.04 097	19.47 82	41.96 44	1.35 318
740	547 600	27.20 29	86.02 33	405 224 000	9.04 504	19.48 70	41.98 34	1.35 135
741	549 081	27.22 13	86.08 14	406 869 021	9.04 911	19.49 57	42.00 23	1.34 953
742	550 564	27.23 97	86.13 94	408 518 488	9.05 318	19.50 45	42.02 12	1.34 771
743	552 049	27.25 80	86.19 74	410 172 407	9.05 725	19.51 32	42.04 00	1.34 590
744	553 536	27.27 64	86.25 54	411 830 784	9.06 131	19.52 20	42.05 89	1.34 409
745	555 025	27.29 47	86.31 34	413 493 625	9.06 537	19.53 07	42.07 77	1.34 228
746	556 516	27.31 30	86.37 13	415 160 936	9.06 942	19.53 95	42.09 65	1.34 048
747	558 009	27.33 13	86.42 92	416 832 723	9.07 347	19.54 82	42.11 53	1.33 869
748	559 504	27.34 96	86.48 70	418 508 992	9.07 752	19.55 69	42.13 41	1.33 690
749	561 001	27.36 79	86.54 48	420 189 749	9.08 156	19.56 56	42.15 29	1.33 511
750	562 500	27.38 61	86.60 25	421 875 000	9.08 560	19.57 43	42.17 16	1.33 333
N	N²	√N	√10N	N³	∛N	∛10N	∛100N	1000 /N

750 — Powers, Roots, Reciprocals — 800

N	N^2	$\sqrt{N}$	$\sqrt{10N}$	N^3	$\sqrt[3]{N}$	$\sqrt[3]{10N}$	$\sqrt[3]{100N}$	1000/N
750	562 500	27.38 61	86.60 25	421 875 000	9.08 560	19.57 43	42.17 16	1.33 333
751	564 001	27.40 44	86.66 03	423 564 751	9.08 964	19.58 30	42.19 04	1.33 156
752	565 504	27.42 26	86.71 79	425 259 008	9.09 367	19.59 17	42.20 91	1.32 979
753	567 009	27.44 08	86.77 56	426 957 777	9.09 770	19.60 04	42.22 78	1.32 802
754	568 516	27.45 91	86.83 32	428 661 064	9.10 173	19.60 91	42.24 65	1.32 626
755	570 025	27.47 73	86.89 07	430 368 875	9.10 575	19.61 77	42.26 51	1.32 450
756	571 536	27.49 55	86.94 83	432 081 216	9.10 977	19.62 64	42.28 38	1.32 275
757	573 049	27.51 36	87.00 57	433 798 093	9.11 378	19.63 50	42.30 24	1.32 100
758	574 564	27.53 18	87.06 32	435 519 512	9.11 779	19.64 37	42.32 10	1.31 926
759	576 081	27.55 00	87.12 06	437 245 479	9.12 180	19.65 23	42.33 96	1.31 752
760	577 600	27.56 81	87.17 80	438 976 000	9.12 581	19.66 10	42.35 82	1.31 579
761	579 121	27.58 62	87.23 53	440 711 081	9.12 981	19.66 96	42.37 68	1.31 406
762	580 644	27.60 43	87.29 26	442 450 728	9.13 380	19.67 82	42.39 54	1.31 234
763	582 169	27.62 25	87.34 99	444 194 947	9.13 780	19.68 68	42.41 39	1.31 062
764	583 696	27.64 05	87.40 71	445 943 744	9.14 179	19.69 54	42.43 24	1.30 890
765	585 225	27.65 86	87.46 43	447 697 125	9.14 577	19.70 40	42.45 09	1.30 719
766	586 756	27.67 67	87.52 14	449 455 096	9.14 976	19.71 26	42.46 94	1.30 548
767	588 289	27.69 48	87.57 85	451 217 663	9.15 374	19.72 11	42.48 79	1.30 378
768	589 824	27.71 28	87.63 56	452 984 832	9.15 771	19.72 97	42.50 63	1.30 208
769	591 361	27.73 08	87.69 26	454 756 609	9.16 169	19.73 83	42.52 48	1.30 039
770	592 900	27.74 89	87.74 96	456 533 000	9.16 566	19.74 68	42.54 32	1.29 870
771	594 441	27.76 69	87.80 66	458 314 011	9.16 962	19.75 54	42.56 16	1.29 702
772	595 984	27.78 49	87.86 35	460 099 648	9.17 359	19.76 39	42.58 00	1.29 534
773	597 529	27.80 29	87.92 04	461 889 917	9.17 754	19.77 24	42.59 84	1.29 366
774	599 076	27.82 09	87.97 73	463 684 824	9.18 150	19.78 09	42.61 67	1.29 199
775	600 625	27.83 88	88.03 41	465 484 375	9.18 545	19.78 95	42.63 51	1.29 032
776	602 176	27.85 68	88.09 09	467 288 576	9.18 940	19.79 80	42.65 34	1.28 866
777	603 729	27.87 47	88.14 76	469 097 433	9.19 335	19.80 65	42.67 17	1.28 700
778	605 284	27.89 27	88.20 43	470 910 952	9.19 729	19.81 50	42.69 00	1.28 535
779	606 841	27.91 06	88.26 10	472 729 139	9.20 123	19.82 34	42.70 83	1.28 370
780	608 400	27.92 85	88.31 76	474 552 000	9.20 516	19.83 19	42.72 66	1.28 205
781	609 961	27.94 64	88.37 42	476 379 541	9.20 910	19.84 04	42.74 48	1.28 041
782	611 524	27.96 43	88.43 08	478 211 768	9.21 303	19.84 89	42.76 31	1.27 877
783	613 089	27.98 21	88.48 73	480 048 687	9.21 695	19.85 73	42.78 13	1.27 714
784	614 656	28.00 00	88.54 38	481 890 304	9.22 087	19.86 58	42.79 95	1.27 551
785	616 225	28.01 79	88.60 02	483 736 625	9.22 479	19.87 42	42.81 77	1.27 389
786	617 796	28.03 57	88.65 66	485 587 656	9.22 871	19.88 26	42.83 59	1.27 226
787	619 369	28.05 35	88.71 30	487 443 403	9.23 262	19.89 11	42.85 40	1.27 065
788	620 944	28.07 13	88.76 94	489 303 872	9.23 653	19.89 95	42.87 22	1.26 904
789	622 521	28.08 91	88.82 57	491 169 069	9.24 043	19.90 79	42.89 03	1.26 743
790	624 100	28.10 69	88.88 19	493 039 000	9.24 434	19.91 63	42.90 84	1.26 582
791	625 681	28.12 47	88.93 82	494 913 671	9.24 823	19.92 47	42.92 65	1.26 422
792	627 264	28.14 25	88.99 44	496 793 088	9.25 213	19.93 31	42.94 46	1.26 263
793	628 849	28.16 03	89.05 05	498 677 257	9.25 602	19.94 15	42.96 27	1.26 103
794	630 436	28.17 80	89.10 67	500 566 184	9.25 991	19.94 99	42.98 07	1.25 945
795	632 025	28.19 57	89.16 28	502 459 875	9.26 380	19.95 82	42.99 87	1.25 786
796	633 616	28.21 35	89.21 88	504 358 336	9.26 768	19.96 66	43.01 68	1.25 628
797	635 209	28.23 12	89.27 49	506 261 573	9.27 156	19.97 50	43.03 48	1.25 471
798	636 804	28.24 89	89.33 08	508 169 592	9.27 544	19.98 33	43.05 28	1.25 313
799	638 401	28.26 66	89.38 68	510 082 399	9.27 931	19.99 17	43.07 07	1.25 156
800	640 000	28.28 43	89.44 27	512 000 000	9.28 318	20.00 00	43.08 87	1.25 000
N	N^2	$\sqrt{N}$	$\sqrt{10N}$	N^3	$\sqrt[3]{N}$	$\sqrt[3]{10N}$	$\sqrt[3]{100N}$	1000/N

800 — Powers, Roots, Reciprocals — 850

N	N²	√N̄	√1̄0̄N̄	N³	∛N̄	∛1̄0̄N̄	∛1̄0̄0̄N̄	1000/N
800	640 000	28.28 43	89.44 27	512 000 000	9.28 318	20.00 00	43.08 87	1.25 000
801	641 601	28.30 19	89.49 86	513 922 401	9.28 704	20.00 83	43.10 66	1.24 844
802	643 204	28.31 96	89.55 45	515 849 608	9.29 091	20.01 67	43.12 46	1.24 688
803	644 809	28.33 73	89.61 03	517 781 627	9.29 477	20.02 50	43.14 25	1.24 533
.804	646 416	28.35 49	89.66 60	519 718 464	9.29 862	20.03 33	43.16 04	1.24 378
805	648 025	28.37 25	89.72 18	521 660 125	9.30 248	20.04 16	43.17 83	1.24 224
806	649 636	28.39 01	89.77 75	523 606 616	9.30 633	20.04 99	43.19 61	1.24 069
807	651 249	28.40 77	89.83 32	525 557 943	9.31 018	20.05 82	43.21 40	1.23 916
808	652 864	28.42 53	89.88 88	527 514 112	9.31 402	20.06 64	43.23 18	1.23 762
809	654 481	28.44 29	89.94 44	529 475 129	9.31 786	20.07 47	43.24 97	1.23 609
810	656 100	28.46 05	90.00 00	531 441 000	9.32 170	20.08 30	43.26 75	1.23 457
811	657 721	28.47 81	90.05 55	533 411 731	9.32 553	20.09 12	43.28 53	1.23 305
812	659 344	28.49 56	90.11 10	535 387 328	9.32 936	20.09 95	43.30 31	1.23 153
813	660 969	28.51 32	90.16 65	537 367 797	9.33 319	20.10 78	43.32 08	1.23 001
814	662 596	28.53 07	90.22 19	539 353 144	9.33 702	20.11 60	43.33 86	1.22 850
815	664 225	28.54 82	90.27 74	541 343 375	9.34 084	20.12 42	43.35 63	1.22 699
816	665 856	28.56 57	90.33 27	543 338 496	9.34 466	20.13 25	43.37 41	1.22 549
817	667 489	28.58 32	90.38 81	545 338 513	9.34 847	20.14 07	43.39 18	1.22 399
818	669 124	28.60 07	90.44 34	547 343 432	9.35 229	20.14 89	43.40 95	1.22 249
819	670 761	28.61 82	90.49 86	549 353 259	9.35 610	20.15 71	43.42 71	1.22 100
820	672 400	28.63 56	90.55 39	551 368 000	9.35 990	20.16 53	43.44 48	1.21 951
821	674 041	28.65 31	90.60 91	553 387 661	9.36 370	20.17 35	43.46 25	1.21 803
822	675 684	28.67 05	90.66 42	555 412 248	9.36 751	20.18 17	43.48 01	1.21 655
823	677 329	28.68 80	90.71 93	557 441 767	9.37 130	20.18 99	43.49 77	1.21 507
824	678 976	28.70 54	90.77 44	559 476 224	9.37 510	20.19 80	43.51 53	1.21 359
825	680 625	28.72 28	90.82 95	561 515 625	9.37 889	20.20 62	43.53 29	1.21 212
826	682 276	28.74 02	90.88 45	563 559 976	9.38 268	20.21 44	43.55 05	1.21 065
827	683 929	28.75 76	90.93 95	565 609 283	9.38 646	20.22 25	43.56 81	1.20 919
828	685 584	28.77 50	90.99 45	567 663 552	9.39 024	20.23 07	43.58 56	1.20 773
829	687 241	28.79 24	91.04 94	569 722 789	9.39 402	20.23 88	43.60 32	1.20 627
830	688 900	28.80 97	91.10 43	571 787 000	9.39 780	20.24 69	43.62 07	1.20 482
831	690 561	28.82 71	91.15 92	573 856 191	9.40 157	20.25 51	43.63 82	1.20 337
832	692 224	28.84 44	91.21 40	575 930 368	9.40 534	20.26 32	43.65 57	1.20 192
833	693 889	28.86 17	91.26 88	578 009 537	9.40 911	20.27 13	43.67 32	1.20 048
834	695 556	28.87 91	91.32 36	580 093 704	9.41 287	20.27 94	43.69 07	1.19 904
835	697 225	28.89 64	91.37 83	582 182 875	9.41 663	20.28 75	43.70 81	1.19 760
836	698 896	28.91 37	91.43 30	584 277 056	9.42 039	20.29 56	43.72 56	1.19 617
837	700 569	28.93 10	91.48 77	586 376 253	9.42 414	20.30 37	43.74 30	1.19 474
838	702 244	28.94 82	91.54 23	588 480 472	9.42 789	20.31 18	43.76 04	1.19 332
839	703 921	28.96 55	91.59 69	590 589 719	9.43 164	20.31 99	43.77 78	1.19 190
840	705 600	28.98 28	91.65 15	592 704 000	9.43 539	20.32 79	43.79 52	1.19 048
841	707 281	29.00 00	91.70 61	594 823 321	9.43 913	20.33 60	43.81 26	1.18 906
842	708 964	29.01 72	91.76 06	596 947 688	9.44 287	20.34 40	43.82 99	1.18 765
843	710 649	29.03 45	91.81 50	599 077 107	9.44 661	20.35 21	43.84 73	1.18 624
844	712 336	29.05 17	91.86 95	601 211 584	9.45 034	20.36 01	43.86 46	1.18 483
845	714 025	29.06 89	91.92 39	603 351 125	9.45 407	20.36 82	43.88 19	1.18 343
846	715 716	29.08 61	91.97 83	605 495 736	9.45 780	20.37 62	43.89 92	1.18 203
847	717 409	29.10 33	92.03 26	607 645 423	9.46 152	20.38 42	43.91 65	1.18 064
848	719 104	29.12 04	92.08 69	609 800 192	9.46 525	20.39 23	43.93 38	1.17 925
849	720 801	29.13 76	92.14 12	611 960 049	9.46 897	20.40 03	43.95 10	1.17 786
850	722 500	29.15 48	92.19 54	614 125 000	9.47 268	20.40 83	43.96 83	1.17 647
N	N²	√N̄	√1̄0̄N̄	N³	∛N̄	∛1̄0̄N̄	∛1̄0̄0̄N̄	1000/N

850 — Powers, Roots, Reciprocals — 900

N	N^2	$\sqrt{N}$	$\sqrt{10N}$	N^3	$\sqrt[3]{N}$	$\sqrt[3]{10N}$	$\sqrt[3]{100N}$	$1000/N$
850	722 500	29.15 48	92.19 54	614 125 000	9.47 268	20.40 83	43.96 83	1.17 647
851	724 201	29.17 19	92.24 97	616 295 051	9.47 640	20.41 63	43.98 55	1.17 509
852	725 904	29.18 90	92.30 38	618 470 208	9.48 011	20.42 43	44.00 28	1.17 371
853	727 609	29.20 62	92.35 80	620 650 477	9.48 381	20.43 23	44.02 00	1.17 233
854	729 316	29.22 33	92.41 21	622 835 864	9.48 752	20.44 02	44.03 72	1.17 096
855	731 025	29.24 04	92.46 62	625 026 375	9.49 122	20.44 82	44.05 43	1.16 959
856	732 736	29.25 75	92.52 03	627 222 016	9.49 492	20.45 62	44.07 15	1.16 822
857	734 449	29.27 46	92.57 43	629 422 793	9.49 861	20.46 41	44.08 87	1.16 686
858	736 164	29.29 16	92.62 83	631 628 712	9.50 231	20.47 21	44.10 58	1.16 550
859	737 881	29.30 87	92.68 23	633 839 779	9.50 600	20.48 01	44.12 29	1.16 414
860	739 600	29.32 58	92.73 62	636 056 000	9.50 969	20.48 80	44.14 00	1.16 279
861	741 321	29.34 28	92.79 01	638 277 381	9.51 337	20.49 59	44.15 71	1.16 144
862	743 044	29.35 98	92.84 40	640 503 928	9.51 705	20.50 39	44.17 42	1.16 009
863	744 769	29.37 69	92.89 78	642 735 647	9.52 073	20.51 18	44.19 13	1.15 875
864	746 496	29.39 39	92.95 16	644 972 544	9.52 441	20.51 97	44.20 84	1.15 741
865	748 225	29.41 09	93.00 54	647 214 625	9.52 808	20.52 76	44.22 54	1.15 607
866	749 956	29.42 79	93.05 91	649 461 896	9.53 175	20.53 55	44.24 25	1.15 473
867	751 689	29.44 49	93.11 28	651 714 363	9.53 542	20.54 34	44.25 95	1.15 340
868	753 424	29.46 18	93.16 65	653 972 032	9.53 908	20.55 13	44.27 65	1.15 207
869	755 161	29.47 88	93.22 02	656 234 909	9.54 274	20.55 92	44.29 35	1.15 075
870	756 900	29.49 58	93.27 38	658 503 000	9.54 640	20.56 71	44.31 05	1.14 943
871	758 641	29.51 27	93.32 74	660 776 311	9.55 006	20.57 50	44.32 74	1.14 811
872	760 384	29.52 96	93.38 09	663 054 848	9.55 371	20.58 28	44.34 44	1.14 679
873	762 129	29.54 66	93.43 45	665 338 617	9.55 736	20.59 07	44.36 13	1.14 548
874	763 876	29.56 35	93.48 80	667 627 624	9.56 101	20.59 86	44.37 83	1.14 416
875	765 625	29.58 04	93.54 14	669 921 875	9.56 466	20.60 64	44.39 52	1.14 286
876	767 376	29.59 73	93.59 49	672 221 376	9.56 830	20.61 43	44.41 21	1.14 155
877	769 129	29.61 42	93.64 83	674 526 133	9.57 194	20.62 21	44.42 90	1.14 025
878	770 884	29.63 11	93.70 17	676 836 152	9.57 557	20.62 99	44.44 59	1.13 895
879	772 641	29.64 79	93.75 50	679 151 439	9.57 921	20.63 78	44.46 27	1.13 766
880	774 400	29.66 48	93.80 83	681 472 000	9.58 284	20.64 56	44.47 96	1.13 636
881	776 161	29.68 16	93.86 16	683 797 841	9.58 647	20.65 34	44.49 64	1.13 507
882	777 924	29.69 85	93.91 49	686 128 968	9.59 009	20.66 12	44.51 33	1.13 379
883	779 689	29.71 53	93.96 81	688 465 387	9.59 372	20.66 90	44.53 01	1.13 250
884	781 456	29.73 21	94.02 13	690 807 104	9.59 734	20.67 68	44.54 69	1.13 122
885	783 225	29.74 89	94.07 44	693 154 125	9.60 095	20.68 46	44.56 37	1.12 994
886	784 996	29.76 58	94.12 76	695 506 456	9.60 457	20.69 24	44.58 05	1.12 867
887	786 769	29.78 25	94.18 07	697 864 103	9.60 818	20.70 02	44.59 72	1.12 740
888	788 544	29.79 93	94.23 38	700 227 072	9.61 179	20.70 80	44.61 40	1.12 613
889	790 321	29.81 61	94.28 68	702 595 369	9.61 540	20.71 57	44.63 07	1.12 486
890	792 100	29.83 29	94.33 98	704 969 000	9.61 900	20.72 35	44.64 75	1.12 360
891	793 881	29.84 96	94.39 28	707 347 971	9.62 260	20.73 13	44.66 42	1.12 233
892	795 664	29.86 64	94.44 58	709 732 288	9.62 620	20.73 90	44.68 09	1.12 108
893	797 449	29.88 31	94.49 87	712 121 957	9.62 980	20.74 68	44.69 76	1.11 982
894	799 236	29.89 98	94.55 16	714 516 984	9.63 339	20.75 45	44.71 42	1.11 857
895	801 025	29.91 66	94.60 44	716 917 375	9.63 698	20.76 22	44.73 09	1.11 732
896	802 816	29.93 33	94.65 73	719 323 136	9.64 057	20.77 00	44.74 76	1.11 607
897	804 609	29.95 00	94.71 01	721 734 273	9.64 415	20.77 77	44.76 42	1.11 483
898	806 404	29.96 66	94.76 29	724 150 792	9.64 774	20.78 54	44.78 08	1.11 359
899	808 201	29.98 33	94.81 56	726 572 699	9.65 132	20.79 31	44.79 74	1.11 235
900	810 000	30.00 00	94.86 83	729 000 000	9.65 489	20.80 08	44.81 40	1.11 111
N	N^2	$\sqrt{N}$	$\sqrt{10N}$	N^3	$\sqrt[3]{N}$	$\sqrt[3]{10N}$	$\sqrt[3]{100N}$	$1000/N$

900 — Powers, Roots, Reciprocals — 950

N	N²	√N	√10N	N³	∛N	∛10N	∛100N	1000 /N
900	810 000	30.00 00	94.86 83	729 000 000	9.65 489	20.80 08	44.81 40	1.11 111
901	811 801	30.01 67	94.92 10	731 432 701	9.65 847	20.80 85	44.83 06	1.10 988
902	813 604	30.03 33	94.97 37	733 870 808	9.66 204	20.81 62	44.84 72	1.10 865
903	815 409	30.05 00	95.02 63	736 314 327	9.66 561	20.82 39	44.86 38	1.10 742
904	817 216	30.06 66	95.07 89	738 763 264	9.66 918	20.83 16	44.88 03	1.10 619
905	819 025	30.08 32	95.13 15	741 217 625	9.67 274	20.83 93	44.89 69	1.10 497
906	820 836	30.09 98	95.18 40	743 677 416	9.67 630	20.84 70	44.91 34	1.10 375
907	822 649	30.11 64	95.23 65	746 142 643	9.67 986	20.85 46	44.92 99	1.10 254
908	824 464	30.13 30	95.28 90	748 613 312	9.68 342	20.86 23	44.94 64	1.10 132
909	826 281	30.14 96	95.34 15	751 089 429	9.68 697	20.86 99	44.96 29	1.10 011
910	828 100	30.16 62	95.39 39	753 571 000	9.69 052	20.87 76	44.97 94	1.09 890
911	829 921	30.18 28	95.44 63	756 058 031	9.69 407	20.88 52	44.99 59	1.09 769
912	831 744	30.19 93	95.49 87	758 550 528	9.69 762	20.89 29	45.01 23	1.09 649
913	833 569	30.21 59	95.55 10	761 048 497	9.70 116	20.90 05	45.02 88	1.09 529
914	835 396	30.23 24	95.60 33	763 551 944	9.70 470	20.90 81	45.04 52	1.09 409
915	837 225	30.24 90	95.65 56	766 060 875	9.70 824	20.91 58	45.06 16	1.09 290
916	839 056	30.26 55	95.70 79	768 575 296	9.71 177	20.92 34	45.07 81	1.09 170
917	840 889	30.28 20	95.76 01	771 095 213	9.71 531	20.93 10	45.09 45	1.09 051
918	842 724	30.29 85	95.81 23	773 620 632	9.71 884	20.93 86	45.11 08	1.08 932
919	844 561	30.31 50	95.86 45	776 151 559	9.72 236	20.94 62	45.12 72	1.08 814
920	846 400	30.33 15	95.91 66	778 688 000	9.72 589	20.95 38	45.14 36	1.08 696
921	848 241	30.34 80	95.96 87	781 229 961	9.72 941	20.96 14	45.15 99	1.08 578
922	850 084	30.36 45	96.02 08	783 777 448	9.73 293	20.96 90	45.17 63	1.08 460
923	851 929	30.38 09	96.07 29	786 330 467	9.73 645	20.97 65	45.19 26	1.08 342
924	853 776	30.39 74	96.12 49	788 889 024	9.73 996	20.98 41	45.20 89	1.08 225
925	855 625	30.41 38	96.17 69	791 453 125	9.74 348	20.99 17	45.22 52	1.08 108
926	857 476	30.43 02	96.22 89	794 022 776	9.74 699	20.99 92	45.24 15	1.07 991
927	859 329	30.44 67	96.28 08	796 597 983	9.75 049	21.00 68	45.25 78	1.07 875
928	861 184	30.46 31	96.33 28	799 178 752	9.75 400	21.01 44	45.27 40	1.07 759
929	863 041	30.47 95	96.38 46	801 765 089	9.75 750	21.02 19	45.29 03	1.07 643
930	864 900	30.49 59	96.43 65	804 357 000	9.76 100	21.02 94	45.30 65	1.07 527
931	866 761	30.51 23	96.48 83	806 954 491	9.76 450	21.03 70	45.32 28	1.07 411
932	868 624	30.52 87	96.54 01	809 557 568	9.76 799	21.04 45	45.33 90	1.07 296
933	870 489	30.54 50	96.59 19	812 166 237	9.77 148	21.05 20	45.35 52	1.07 181
934	872 356	30.56 14	96.64 37	814 780 504	9.77 497	21.05 95	45.37 14	1.07 066
935	874 225	30.57 78	96.69 54	817 400 375	9.77 846	21.06 71	45.38 76	1.06 952
936	876 096	30.59 41	96.74 71	820 025 856	9.78 195	21.07 46	45.40 38	1.06 838
937	877 969	30.61 05	96.79 88	822 656 953	9.78 543	21.08 21	45.41 99	1.06 724
938	879 844	30.62 68	96.85 04	825 293 672	9.78 891	21.08 96	45.43 61	1.06 610
939	881 721	30.64 31	96.90 20	827 936 019	9.79 239	21.09 71	45.45 22	1.06 496
940	883 600	30.65 94	96.95 36	830 584 000	9.79 586	21.10 45	45.46 84	1.06 383
941	885 481	30.67 57	97.00 52	833 237 621	9.79 933	21.11 20	45.48 45	1.06 270
942	887 364	30.69 20	97.05 67	835 896 888	9.80 280	21.11 95	45.50 06	1.06 157
943	889 249	30.70 83	97.10 82	838 561 807	9.80 627	21.12 70	45.51 67	1.06 045
944	891 136	30.72 46	97.15 97	841 232 384	9.80 974	21.13 44	45.53 28	1.05 932
945	893 025	30.74 09	97.21 11	843 908 625	9.81 320	21.14 19	45.54 88	1.05 820
946	894 916	30.75 71	97.26 25	846 590 536	9.81 666	21.14 94	45.56 49	1.05 708
947	896 809	30.77 34	97.31 39	849 278 123	9.82 012	21.15 68	45.58 09	1.05 597
948	898 704	30.78 96	97.36 53	851 971 392	9.82 357	21.16 42	45.59 70	1.05 485
949	900 601	30.80 58	97.41 66	854 670 349	9.82 703	21.17 17	45.61 30	1.05 374
950	902 500	30.82 21	97.46 79	857 375 000	9.83 048	21.17 91	45.62 90	1.05 263
N	N²	√N	√10N	N³	∛N	∛10N	∛100N	1000 /N

950 — Powers, Roots, Reciprocals — 1000

N	N^2	$\sqrt{N}$	$\sqrt{10N}$	N^3	$\sqrt[3]{N}$	$\sqrt[3]{10N}$	$\sqrt[3]{100N}$	1000 /N
950	902 500	30.82 21	97.46 79	857 375 000	9.83 048	21.17 91	45.62 90	1.05 263
951	904 401	30.83 83	97.51 92	860 085 351	9.83 392	21.18 65	45.64 50	1.05 152
952	906 304	30.85 45	97.57 05	862 801 408	9.83 737	21.19 40	45.66 10	1.05 042
953	908 209	30.87 07	97.62 17	865 523 177	9.84 081	21.20 14	45.67 70	1.04 932
954	910 116	30.88 69	97.67 29	868 250 664	9.84 425	21.20 88	45.69 30	1.04 822
955	912 025	30.90 31	97.72 41	870 983 875	9.84 769	21.21 62	45.70 89	1.04 712
956	913 936	30.91 92	97.77 53	873 722 816	9.85 113	21.22 36	45.72 49	1.04 603
957	915 849	30.93 54	97.82 64	876 467 493	9.85 456	21.23 10	45.74 08	1.04 493
958	917 764	30.95 16	97.87 75	879 217 912	9.85 799	21.23 84	45.75 67	1.04 384
959	919 681	30.96 77	97.92 85	881 974 079	9.86 142	21.24 58	45.77 27	1.04 275
960	921 600	30.98 39	97.97 96	884 736 000	9.86 485	21.25 32	45.78 86	1.04 167
961	923 521	31.00 00	98.03 06	887 503 681	9.86 827	21.26 05	45.80 45	1.04 058
962	925 444	31.01 61	98.08 16	890 277 128	9.87 169	21.26 79	45.82 04	1.03 950
963	927 369	31.03 22	98.13 26	893 056 347	9.87 511	21.27 53	45.83 62	1.03 842
964	929 296	31.04 83	98.18 35	895 841 344	9.87 853	21.28 26	45.85 21	1.03 734
965	931 225	31.06 44	98.23 44	898 632 125	9.88 195	21.29 00	45.86 79	1.03 627
966	933 156	31.08 05	98.28 53	901 428 696	9.88 536	21.29 74	45.88 38	1.03 520
967	935 089	31.09 66	98.33 62	904 231 063	9.88 877	21.30 47	45.89 96	1.03 413
968	937 024	31.11 27	98.38 70	907 039 232	9.89 217	21.31 20	45.91 54	1.03 306
969	938 961	31.12 88	98.43 78	909 853 209	9.89 558	21.31 94	45.93 12	1.03 199
970	940 900	31.14 48	98.48 86	912 673 000	9.89 898	21.32 67	45.94 70	1.03 093
971	942 841	31.16 09	98.53 93	915 498 611	9.90 238	21.33 40	45.96 28	1.02 987
972	944 784	31.17 69	98.59 01	918 330 048	9.90 578	21.34 14	45.97 86	1.02 881
973	946 729	31.19 29	98.64 08	921 167 317	9.90 918	21.34 87	45.99 43	1.02 775
974	948 676	31.20 90	98.69 14	924 010 424	9.91 257	21.35 60	46.01 01	1.02 669
975	950 625	31.22 50	98.74 21	926 859 375	9.91 596	21.36 33	46.02 58	1.02 564
976	952 576	31.24 10	98.79 27	929 714 176	9.91 935	21.37 06	46.04 16	1.02 459
977	954 529	31.25 70	98.84 33	932 574 833	9.92 274	21.37 79	46.05 73	1.02 354
978	956 484	31.27 30	98.89 39	935 441 352	9.92 612	21.38 52	46.07 30	1.02 249
979	958 441	31.28 90	98.94 44	938 313 739	9.92 950	21.39 25	46.08 87	1.02 145
980	960 400	31.30 50	98.99 49	941 192 000	9.93 288	21.39 97	46.10 44	1.02 041
981	962 361	31.32 09	99.04 54	944 076 141	9.93 626	21.40 70	46.12 00	1.01 937
982	964 324	31.33 69	99.09 59	946 966 168	9.93 964	21.41 43	46.13 57	1.01 833
983	966 289	31.35 28	99.14 64	949 862 087	9.94 301	21.42 16	46.15 14	1.01 729
984	968 256	31.36 88	99.19 68	952 763 904	9.94 638	21.42 88	46.16 70	1.01 626
985	970 225	31.38 47	99.24 72	955 671 625	9.94 975	21.43 61	46.18 26	1.01 523
986	972 196	31.40 06	99.29 75	958 585 256	9.95 311	21.44 33	46.19 83	1.01 420
987	974 169	31.41 66	99.34 79	961 504 803	9.95 648	21.45 06	46.21 39	1.01 317
988	976 144	31.43 25	99.39 82	964 430 272	9.95 984	21.45 78	46.22 95	1.01 215
989	978 121	31.44 84	99.44 85	967 361 669	9.96 320	21.46 51	46.24 51	1.01 112
990	980 100	31.46 43	99.49 87	970 299 000	9.96 655	21.47 23	46.26 07	1.01 010
991	982 081	31.48 02	99.54 90	973 242 271	9.96 991	21.47 95	46.27 62	1.00 908
992	984 064	31.49 60	99.59 92	976 191 488	9.97 326	21.48 67	46.29 18	1.00 806
993	986 049	31.51 19	99.64 94	979 146 657	9.97 661	21.49 40	46.30 73	1.00 705
994	988 036	31.52 78	99.69 95	982 107 784	9.97 996	21.50 12	46.32 29	1.00 604
995	990 025	31.54 36	99.74 97	985 074 875	9.98 331	21.50 84	46.33 84	1.00 503
996	992 016	31.55 95	99.79 98	988 047 936	9.98 665	21.51 56	46.35 39	1.00 402
997	994 009	31.57 53	99.84 99	991 026 973	9.98 999	21.52 28	46.36 94	1.00 301
998	996 004	31.59 11	99.89 99	994 011 992	9.99 333	21.53 00	46.38 49	1.00 200
999	998 001	31.60 70	99.95 00	997 002 999	9.99 667	21.53 72	46.40 04	1.00 100
1000	1000 000	31.62 28	100.00 00	1000 000 000	10.00 000	21.54 43	46.41 59	1.00 000
N	N^2	$\sqrt{N}$	$\sqrt{10N}$	N^3	$\sqrt[3]{N}$	$\sqrt[3]{10N}$	$\sqrt[3]{100N}$	1000 /N

1.00 — Four-Place Natural Logarithms — 5.59

N	.00	.01	.02	.03	.04	.05	.06	.07	.08	.09
1.0	0.0000	0.0100	0.0198	0.0296	0.0392	0.0488	0.0583	0.0677	0.0770	0.0862
1.1	0.0953	0.1044	0.1133	0.1222	0.1310	0.1398	0.1484	0.1570	0.1655	0.1740
1.2	0.1823	0.1906	0.1989	0.2070	0.2151	0.2231	0.2311	0.2390	0.2469	0.2546
1.3	0.2624	0.2700	0.2776	0.2852	0.2927	0.3001	0.3075	0.3148	0.3221	0.3293
1.4	0.3365	0.3436	0.3507	0.3577	0.3646	0.3716	0.3784	0.3853	0.3920	0.3988
1.5	0.4055	0.4121	0.4187	0.4253	0.4318	0.4383	0.4447	0.4511	0.4574	0.4637
1.6	0.4700	0.4762	0.4824	0.4886	0.4947	0.5008	0.5068	0.5128	0.5188	0.5247
1.7	0.5306	0.5365	0.5423	0.5481	0.5539	0.5596	0.5653	0.5710	0.5766	0.5822
1.8	0.5878	0.5933	0.5988	0.6043	0.6098	0.6152	0.6206	0.6259	0.6313	0.6366
1.9	0.6419	0.6471	0.6523	0.6575	0.6627	0.6678	0.6729	0.6780	0.6831	0.6881
2.0	0.6931	0.6981	0.7031	0.7080	0.7129	0.7178	0.7227	0.7275	0.7324	0.7372
2.1	0.7419	0.7467	0.7514	0.7561	0.7608	0.7655	0.7701	0.7747	0.7793	0.7839
2.2	0.7885	0.7930	0.7975	0.8020	0.8065	0.8109	0.8154	0.8198	0.8242	0.8286
2.3	0.8329	0.8372	0.8416	0.8459	0.8502	0.8544	0.8587	0.8629	0.8671	0.8713
2.4	0.8755	0.8796	0.8838	0.8879	0.8920	0.8961	0.9002	0.9042	0.9083	0.9123
2.5	0.9163	0.9203	0.9243	0.9282	0.9322	0.9361	0.9400	0.9439	0.9478	0.9517
2.6	0.9555	0.9594	0.9632	0.9670	0.9708	0.9746	0.9783	0.9821	0.9858	0.9895
2.7	0.9933	0.9969	1.0006	1.0043	1.0080	1.0116	1.0152	1.0188	1.0225	1.0260
2.8	1.0296	1.0332	1.0367	1.0403	1.0438	1.0473	1.0508	1.0543	1.0578	1.0613
2.9	1.0647	1.0682	1.0716	1.0750	1.0784	1.0818	1.0852	1.0886	1.0919	1.0953
3.0	1.0986	1.1019	1.1053	1.1086	1.1119	1.1151	1.1184	1.1217	1.1249	1.1282
3.1	1.1314	1.1346	1.1378	1.1410	1.1442	1.1474	1.1506	1.1537	1.1569	1.1600
3.2	1.1632	1.1663	1.1694	1.1725	1.1756	1.1787	1.1817	1.1848	1.1878	1.1909
3.3	1.1939	1.1969	1.2000	1.2030	1.2060	1.2090	1.2119	1.2149	1.2179	1.2208
3.4	1.2238	1.2267	1.2296	1.2326	1.2355	1.2384	1.2413	1.2442	1.2470	1.2499
3.5	1.2528	1.2556	1.2585	1.2613	1.2641	1.2669	1.2698	1.2726	1.2754	1.2782
3.6	1.2809	1.2837	1.2865	1.2892	1.2920	1.2947	1.2975	1.3002	1.3029	1.3056
3.7	1.3083	1.3110	1.3137	1.3164	1.3191	1.3218	1.3244	1.3271	1.3297	1.3324
3.8	1.3350	1.3376	1.3403	1.3429	1.3455	1.3481	1.3507	1.3533	1.3558	1.3584
3.9	1.3610	1.3635	1.3661	1.3686	1.3712	1.3737	1.3762	1.3788	1.3813	1.3838
4.0	1.3863	1.3888	1.3913	1.3938	1.3962	1.3987	1.4012	1.4036	1.4061	1.4085
4.1	1.4110	1.4134	1.4159	1.4183	1.4207	1.4231	1.4255	1.4279	1.4303	1.4327
4.2	1.4351	1.4375	1.4398	1.4422	1.4446	1.4469	1.4493	1.4516	1.4540	1.4563
4.3	1.4586	1.4609	1.4633	1.4656	1.4679	1.4702	1.4725	1.4748	1.4770	1.4793
4.4	1.4816	1.4839	1.4861	1.4884	1.4907	1.4929	1.4951	1.4974	1.4996	1.5019
4.5	1.5041	1.5063	1.5085	1.5107	1.5129	1.5151	1.5173	1.5195	1.5217	1.5239
4.6	1.5261	1.5282	1.5304	1.5326	1.5347	1.5369	1.5390	1.5412	1.5433	1.5454
4.7	1.5476	1.5497	1.5518	1.5539	1.5560	1.5581	1.5602	1.5623	1.5644	1.5665
4.8	1.5686	1.5707	1.5728	1.5748	1.5769	1.5790	1.5810	1.5831	1.5851	1.5872
4.9	1.5892	1.5913	1.5933	1.5953	1.5974	1.5994	1.6014	1.6034	1.6054	1.6074
5.0	1.6094	1.6114	1.6134	1.6154	1.6174	1.6194	1.6214	1.6233	1.6253	1.6273
5.1	1.6292	1.6312	1.6332	1.6351	1.6371	1.6390	1.6409	1.6429	1.6448	1.6467
5.2	1.6487	1.6506	1.6525	1.6544	1.6563	1.6582	1.6601	1.6620	1.6639	1.6658
5.3	1.6677	1.6696	1.6715	1.6734	1.6752	1.6771	1.6790	1.6808	1.6827	1.6845
5.4	1.6864	1.6882	1.6901	1.6919	1.6938	1.6956	1.6974	1.6993	1.7011	1.7029
5.5	1.7047	1.7066	1.7084	1.7102	1.7120	1.7138	1.7156	1.7174	1.7192	1.7210
N	.00	.01	.02	.03	.04	.05	.06	.07	.08	.09

$\log_e .1 = .6974{-}3$ $\log_e .01 = .3948{-}5$ $\log_e .001 = .0922{-}7$

5.50 — Four-Place Natural Logarithms — 10.09

N	.00	.01	.02	.03	.04	.05	.06	.07	.08	.09
5.5	1.7047	1.7066	1.7084	1.7102	1.7120	1.7138	1.7156	1.7174	1.7192	1.7210
5.6	1.7228	1.7246	1.7263	1.7281	1.7299	1.7317	1.7334	1.7352	1.7370	1.7387
5.7	1.7405	1.7422	1.7440	1.7457	1.7475	1.7492	1.7509	1.7527	1.7544	1.7561
5.8	1.7579	1.7596	1.7613	1.7630	1.7647	1.7664	1.7681	1.7699	1.7716	1.7733
5.9	1.7750	1.7766	1.7783	1.7800	1.7817	1.7834	1.7851	1.7867	1.7884	1.7901
6.0	1.7918	1.7934	1.7951	1.7967	1.7984	1.8001	1.8017	1.8034	1.8050	1.8066
6.1	1.8083	1.8099	1.8116	1.8132	1.8148	1.8165	1.8181	1.8197	1.8213	1.8229
6.2	'.8245	1.8262	1.8278	1.8294	1.8310	1.8326	1.8342	1.8358	1.8374	1.8390
6.3	1:8405	1.8421	1.8437	1.8453	1.8469	1.8485	1.8500	1.8516	1.8532	1.8547
6.4	1.8563	1.8579	1.8594	1.8610	1.8625	1.8641	1.8656	1.8672	1.8687	1.8703
6.5	1.8718	1.8733	1.8749	1.8764	1.8779	1.8795	1.8810	1.8825	1.8840	1.8856
6.6	1.8871	1.8886	1.8901	1.8916	1.8931	1.8946	1.8961	1.8976	1.8991	1.9006
6.7	1.9021	1.9036	1.9051	1.9066	1.9081	1.9095	1.9110	1.9125	1.9140	1.9155
6.8	1.9169	1.9184	1.9199	1.9213	1.9228	1.9242	1.9257	1.9272	1.9286	1.9301
6.9	1.9315	1.9330	1.9344	1.9359	1.9373	1.9387	1.9402	1.9416	1.9430	1.9445
7.0	1.9459	1.9473	1.9488	1.9502	1.9516	1.9530	1.9544	1.9559	1.9573	1.9587
7.1	1.9601	1.9615	1.9629	1.9643	1.9657	1.9671	1.9685	1.9699	1.9713	1.9727
7.2	1.9741	1.9755	1.9769	1.9782	1.9796	1.9810	1.9824	1.9838	1.9851	1.9865
7.3	1.9879	1.9892	1.9906	1.9920	1.9933	1.9947	1.9961	1.9974	1.9988	2.0001
7.4	2.0015	2.0028	2.0042	2.0055	2.0069	2.0082	2.0096	2.0109	2.0122	2.0136
7.5	2.0149	2.0162	2.0176	2.0189	2.0202	2.0215	2.0229	2.0242	2.0255	2.0268
7.6	2.0281	2.0295	2.0308	2.0321	2.0334	2.0347	2.0360	2.0373	2.0386	2.0399
7.7	2.0412	2.0425	2.0438	2.0451	2.0464	2.0477	2.0490	2.0503	2.0516	2.0528
7.8	2.0541	2.0554	2.0567	2.0580	2.0592	2.0605	2.0618	2.0631	2.0643	2.0656
7.9	2.0669	2.0681	2.0694	2.0707	2.0719	2.0732	2.0744	2.0757	2.0769	2.0782
8.0	2.0794	2.0807	2.0819	2.0832	2.0844	2.0857	2.0869	2.0882	2.0894	2 0906
8.1	2.0919	2.0931	2.0943	2.0956	2.0968	2.0980	2.0992	2.1005	2.1017	2.1029
8.2	2.1041	2.1054	2.1066	2.1078	2.1090	2.1102	2.1114	2.1126	2.1138	2.1150
8.3	2.1163	2.1175	2.1187	2.1199	2.1211	2.1223	2.1235	2.1247	2.1258	2.1270
8.4	2.1282	2.1294	2.1306	2.1318	2.1330	2.1342	2.1353	2.1365	2.1377	2.1389
8.5	2.1401	2.1412	2.1424	2.1436	2.1448	2.1459	2.1471	2.1483	2.1494	2.1506
8.6	2.1518	2.1529	2.1541	2.1552	2.1564	2.1576	2.1587	2.1599	2.1610	2.1622
8.7	2.1633	2.1645	2.1656	2.1668	2.1679	2.1691	2.1702	2.1713	2.1725	2.1736
8.8	2.1748	2.1759	2.1770	2.1782	2.1793	2.1804	2.1815	2.1827	2.1838	2.1849
8.9	2.1861	2.1872	2.1883	2.1894	2.1905	2.1917	2.1928	2.1939	2.1950	2.1961
9.0	2.1972	2.1983	2.1994	2.2006	2.2017	2.2028	2.2039	2.2050	2.2061	2.2072
9.1	2.2083	2.2094	2.2105	2.2116	2.2127	2.2138	2 2148	2.2159	2.2170	2.2181
9.2	2.2192	2.2203	2.2214	2.2225	2.2235	2.2246	2.2257	2.2268	2.2279	2.2289
9.3	2.2300	2.2311	2.2322	2.2332	2.2343	2.2354	2.2364	2.2375	2.2386	2.2396
9.4	2.2407	2.2418	2.2428	2.2439	2.2450	2.2460	2.2471	2.2481	2.2492	2.2502
9.5	2.2513	2.2523	2.2534	2.2544	2.2555	2.2565	2.2576	2.2586	2.2597	2.2607
9.6	2.2618	2.2628	2.2638	2.2649	2.2659	2.2670	2.2680	2.2690	2.2701	2.2711
9.7	2.2721	2.2732	2.2742	2.2752	2.2762	2.2773	2.2783	2.2793	2.2803	2.2814
9.8	2.2824	2.2834	2.2844	2.2854	2.2865	2.2875	2.2885	2.2895	2.2905	2.2915
9.9	2.2925	2.2935	2.2946	2.2956	2.2966	2.2976	2.2986	2.2996	2.3006	2.3016
10.0	2.3026	2.3036	2.3046	2.3056	2.3066	2.3076	2.3086	2.3096	2.3106	2.3115
N	.00	.01	.02	.03	.04	.05	.06	.07	.08	.09

$$\log_e .0001 = .7897 - 10 \qquad \log_e .00001 = .4871 - 12 \qquad \log_e .000\,001 = .1845 - 14$$

10.0 — Four-Place Natural Logarithms — 55.9

N	.0	.1	.2	.3	.4	.5	.6	.7	.8	.9
10	2.3026	2.3125	2.3224	2.3321	2.3418	2.3514	2.3609	2.3702	2.3795	2.3888
11	2.3979	2.4069	2.4159	2.4248	2.4336	2.4423	2.4510	2.4596	2.4681	2.4765
12	2.4849	2.4932	2.5014	2.5096	2.5177	2.5257	2.5337	2.5416	2.5494	2.5572
13	2.5649	2.5726	2.5802	2.5878	2.5953	2.6027	2.6101	2.6174	2.6247	2.6319
14	2.6391	2.6462	2.6532	2.6603	2.6672	2.6741	2.6810	2.6878	2.6946	2.7014
15	2.7081	2.7147	2.7213	2.7279	2.7344	2.7408	2.7473	2.7537	2.7600	2.7663
16	2.7726	2.7788	2.7850	2.7912	2.7973	2.8034	2.8094	2.8154	2.8214	2.8273
17	2.8332	2.8391	2.8449	2.8507	2.8565	2.8622	2.8679	2.8736	2.8792	2.8848
18	2.8904	2.8959	2.9014	2.9069	2.9124	2.9178	2.9232	2.9285	2.9339	2.9392
19	2.9444	2.9497	2.9549	2.9601	2.9653	2.9704	2.9755	2.9806	2.9857	2.9907
20	2.9957	3.0007	3.0057	3.0106	3.0155	3.0204	3.0253	3.0301	3.0350	3.0397
21	3.0445	3.0493	3.0540	3.0587	3.0634	3.0681	3.0727	3.0773	3.0819	3.0865
22	3.0910	3.0956	3.1001	3.1046	3.1091	3.1135	3.1179	3.1224	3.1268	3.1311
23	3.1355	3.1398	3.1442	3.1485	3.1527	3.1570	3.1612	3.1655	3.1697	3.1739
24	3.1781	3.1822	3.1864	3.1905	3.1946	3.1987	3.2027	3.2068	3.2108	3.2149
25	3.2189	3.2229	3.2268	3.2308	3.2347	3.2387	3.2426	3.2465	3.2504	3.2542
26	3.2581	3.2619	3.2658	3.2696	3.2734	3.2771	3.2809	3.2847	3.2884	3.2921
27	3.2958	3.2995	3.3032	3.3069	3.3105	3.3142	3.3178	3.3214	3.3250	3.3286
28	3.3322	3.3358	3.3393	3.3429	3.3464	3.3499	3.3534	3.3569	3.3604	3.3638
29	3.3673	3.3707	3.3742	3.3776	3.3810	3.3844	3.3878	3.3911	3.3945	3.3979
30	3.4012	3.4045	3.4078	3.4111	3.4144	3.4177	3.4210	3.4243	3.4275	3.4308
31	3.4340	3.4372	3.4404	3.4436	3.4468	3.4500	3.4532	3.4563	3.4595	3.4626
32	3.4657	3.4689	3.4720	3.4751	3.4782	3.4812	3.4843	3.4874	3.4904	3.4935
33	3.4965	3.4995	3.5025	3.5056	3.5086	3.5115	3.5145	3.5175	3.5205	3.5234
34	3.5264	3.5293	3.5322	3.5351	3.5381	3.5410	3.5439	3.5467	3.5496	3.5525
35	3.5553	3.5582	3.5610	3.5639	3.5667	3.5695	3.5723	3.5752	3.5779	3.5807
36	3.5835	3.5863	3.5891	3.5918	3.5946	3.5973	3.6000	3.6028	3.6055	3.6082
37	3.6109	3.6136	3.6163	3.6190	3.6217	3.6243	3.6270	3.6297	3.6323	3.6350
38	3.6376	3.6402	3.6428	3.6454	3.6481	3.6507	3.6533	3.6558	3.6584	3.6610
39	3.6636	3.6661	3.6687	3.6712	3.6738	3.6763	3.6788	3.6814	3.6839	3.6864
40	3.6889	3.6914	3.6939	3.6964	3.6988	3.7013	3.7038	3.7062	3.7087	3.7111
41	3.7136	3.7160	3.7184	3.7209	3.7233	3.7257	3.7281	3.7305	3.7329	3.7353
42	3.7377	3.7400	3.7424	3.7448	3.7471	3.7495	3.7519	3.7542	3.7565	3.7589
43	3.7612	3.7635	3.7658	3.7682	3.7705	3.7728	3.7751	3.7773	3.7796	3.7819
44	3.7842	3.7865	3.7887	3.7910	3.7932	3.7955	3.7977	3.8000	3.8022	3.8044
45	3.8067	3.8089	3.8111	3.8133	3.8155	3.8177	3.8199	3.8221	3.8243	3.8265
46	3.8286	3.8308	3.8330	3.8351	3.8373	3.8395	3.8416	3.8437	3.8459	3.8480
47	3.8501	3.8523	3.8544	3.8565	3.8586	3.8607	3.8628	3.8649	3.8670	3.8691
48	3.8712	3.8733	3.8754	3.8774	3.8795	3.8816	3.8836	3.8857	3.8877	3.8898
49	3.8918	3.8939	3.8959	3.8979	3.9000	3.9020	3.9040	3.9060	3.9080	3.9100
50	3.9120	3.9140	3.9160	3.9180	3.9200	3.9220	3.9240	3.9259	3.9279	3.9299
51	3.9318	3.9338	3.9357	3.9377	3.9396	3.9416	3.9435	3.9455	3.9474	3.9493
52	3.9512	3.9532	3.9551	3.9570	3.9589	3.9608	3.9627	3.9646	3.9665	3.9684
53	3.9703	3.9722	3.9741	3.9759	3.9778	3.9797	3.9815	3.9834	3.9853	3.9871
54	3.9890	3.9908	3.9927	3.9945	3.9964	3.9982	4.0000	4.0019	4.0037	4.0055
55	4.0073	4.0091	4.0110	4.0128	4.0146	4.0164	4.0182	4.0200	4.0218	4.0236
N	.0	.1	.2	.3	.4	.5	.6	.7	.8	.9

$\log_e 100 = 4.6052 \qquad \log_e 1000 = 6.9078 \qquad \log_e 10{,}000 = 9.2103$

55.0 — Four-Place Natural Logarithms — 100.9

N	.0	.1	.2	.3	.4	.5	.6	.7	.8	.9
55	4.0073	4.0091	4.0110	4.0128	4.0146	4.0164	4.0182	4.0200	4.0218	4.0236
56	4.0254	4.0271	4.0289	4.0307	4.0325	4.0342	4.0360	4.0378	4.0395	4.0413
57	4.0431	4.0448	4.0466	4.0483	4.0500	4.0518	4.0535	4.0553	4.0570	4.0587
58	4.0604	4.0622	4.0639	4.0656	4.0673	4.0690	4.0707	4.0724	4.0741	4.0758
59	4.0775	4.0792	4.0809	4.0826	4.0843	4.0860	4.0877	4.0893	4.0910	4.0927
60	4.0943	4.0960	4.0977	4.0993	4.1010	4.1026	4.1043	4.1059	4.1076	4.1092
61	4.1109	4.1125	4.1141	4.1158	4.1174	4.1190	4.1207	4.1223	4.1239	4.1255
62	4.1271	4.1287	4.1304	4.1320	4.1336	4.1352	4.1368	4.1384	4.1400	4.1415
63	4.1431	4.1447	4.1463	4.1479	4.1495	4.1510	4.1526	4.1542	4.1558	4.1573
64	4.1589	4.1604	4.1620	4.1636	4.1651	4.1667	4.1682	4.1698	4.1713	4.1728
65	4.1744	4.1759	4.1775	4.1790	4.1805	4.1821	4.1836	4.1851	4.1866	4.1881
66	4.1897	4.1912	4.1927	4.1942	4.1957	4.1972	4.1987	4.2002	4.2017	4.2032
67	4.2047	4.2062	4.2077	4.2092	4.2106	4.2121	4.2136	4.2151	4.2166	4.2180
68	4.2195	4.2210	4.2224	4.2239	4.2254	4.2268	4.2283	4.2297	4.2312	4.2327
69	4.2341	4.2356	4.2370	4.2384	4.2399	4.2413	4.2428	4.2442	4.2456	4.2471
70	4.2485	4.2499	4.2513	4.2528	4.2542	4.2556	4.2570	4.2584	4.2599	4.2613
71	4.2627	4.2641	4.2655	4.2669	4.2683	4.2697	4.2711	4.2725	4.2739	4.2753
72	4.2767	4.2781	4.2794	4.2808	4.2822	4.2836	4.2850	4.2863	4.2877	4.2891
73	4.2905	4.2918	4.2932	4.2946	4.2959	4.2973	4.2986	4.3000	4.3014	4.3027
74	4.3041	4.3054	4.3068	4.3081	4.3095	4.3108	4.3121	4.3135	4.3148	4.3162
75	4.3175	4.3188	4.3202	4.3215	4.3228	4.3241	4.3255	4.3268	4.3281	4.3294
76	4.3307	4.3320	4.3334	4.3347	4.3360	4.3373	4.3386	4.3399	4.3412	4.3425
77	4.3438	4.3451	4.3464	4.3477	4.3490	4.3503	4.3516	4.3529	4.3541	4.3554
78	4.3567	4.3580	4.3593	4.3605	4.3618	4.3631	4.3644	4.3656	4.3669	4.3682
79	4.3694	4.3707	4.3720	4.3732	4.3745	4.3758	4.3770	4.3783	4.3795	4.3808
80	4.3820	4.3833	4.3845	4.3858	4.3870	4.3883	4.3895	4.3907	4.3920	4.3932
81	4.3944	4.3957	4.3969	4.3981	4.3994	4.4006	4.4018	4.4031	4.4043	4.4055
82	4.4067	4.4079	4.4092	4.4104	4.4116	4.4128	4.4140	4.4152	4.4164	4.4176
83	4.4188	4.4200	4.4212	4.4224	4.4236	4.4248	4.4260	4.4272	4.4284	4.4296
84	4.4308	4.4320	4.4332	4.4344	4.4356	4.4368	4.4379	4.4391	4.4403	4.4415
85	4.4427	4.4438	4.4450	4.4462	4.4473	4.4485	4.4497	4.4509	4.4520	4.4532
86	4.4543	4.4555	4.4567	4.4578	4.4590	4.4601	4.4613	4.4625	4.4636	4.4648
87	4.4659	4.4671	4.4682	4.4694	4.4705	4.4716	4.4728	4.4739	4.4751	4.4762
88	4.4773	4.4785	4.4796	4.4807	4.4819	4.4830	4.4841	4.4853	4.4864	4.4875
89	4.4886	4.4898	4.4909	4.4920	4.4931	4.4942	4.4954	4.4965	4.4976	4.4987
90	4.4998	4.5009	4.5020	4.5031	4.5042	4.5053	4.5065	4.5076	4.5087	4.5098
91	4.5109	4.5120	4.5131	4.5142	4.5152	4.5163	4.5174	4.5185	4.5196	4.5207
92	4.5218	4.5229	4.5240	4.5250	4.5261	4.5272	4.5283	4.5294	4.5304	4.5315
93	4.5326	4.5337	4.5347	4.5358	4.5369	4.5380	4.5390	4.5401	4.5412	4.5422
94	4.5433	4.5444	4.5454	4.5465	4.5475	4.5486	4.5497	4.5507	4.5518	4.5528
95	4.5539	4.5549	4.5560	4.5570	4.5581	4.5591	4.5602	4.5612	4.5623	4.5633
96	4.5643	4.5654	4.5664	4.5675	4.5685	4.5695	4.5706	4.5716	4.5726	4.5737
97	4.5747	4.5757	4.5768	4.5778	4.5788	4.5799	4.5809	4.5819	4.5829	4.5839
98	4.5850	4.5860	4.5870	4.5880	4.5890	4.5901	4.5911	4.5921	4.5931	4.5941
99	4.5951	4.5961	4.5971	4.5981	4.5992	4.6002	4.6012	4.6022	4.6032	4.6042
100	4.6052	4.6062	4.6072	4.6082	4.6092	4.6102	4.6112	4.6121	4.6131	4.6141
N	.0	.1	.2	.3	.4	.5	.6	.7	.8	.9

$\log_e 100{,}000 = 11.5129 \qquad \log_e 1{,}000{,}000 = 13.8155 \qquad \log_e 10{,}000{,}000 = 16.1181$

Bibliography

Adams, Carsbie C. *Space Flight.* McGraw-Hill Book Company, Inc., New York, N.Y., 1958, 373 p.

Baker, Robert H. *An Introduction to Astronomy.* D. Van Nostrand Company, Inc., Princeton, N.J., 1962, 364 p.

Committee on Space-Science Oriented Mathematics. *From Here, Where?* Superintendent of Documents, U.S. Government Printing Office, Washington, D.C., 1965, 192 p.

Hobbs, Marvin. *Fundamentals of Rockets, Missiles, and Spacecraft.* John R. Rider Publisher, Inc., New York, N.Y., 1962, 275 p.

Hynek, J. Allen and Anderson, Norman D. *Challenge of the Universe.* Scholastic Book Services, New York, N.Y., 1962, 144 p.

Physical Science Study Committee. *Physics.* D. C. Heath and Co., Boston, Mass., 1960, 656 p.

Polya, George. *Studies in Mathematics, Volume XI,* "Mathematical Methods in Science." A. C. Vroman, Inc., Pasadena, Calif., 1963, 242 p.

Ryabov, Y. *An Elementary Survey of Celestial Mechanics.* Dover Publications, Inc., New York, N.Y., 1961, 165 p.

Seifert, Howard S. and Seifert, Mary Harris. *Orbital Space Flight.* Holt, Rinehart and Winston, Inc., New York, N.Y., 1964, 138 p.

Smith, P. S. *Space Navigation Handbook,* NAVPERS 92988. Superintendent of Documents, U.S. Government Printing Office, Washington, D.C., 1962, 124 p.

Smith, S. W. *Teacher's Handbook of Astronautics.* British Interplanetary Society, London, England, 1963, 115 p.

Tattersfield, D. *Mathematical Problems in Astronautics.* University of London Press, Ltd., London, England, 1964, 67 p.

Vergara, William C. *Mathematics in Everyday Things.* Harper and Brothers, New York, N.Y., 1959, 301 p.

Index